WHO WANTS TO BE A

MILLIONAIRE

WHO WANTS TO BE A

THE QUIZ BOOK

WHO WANTS TO BE A

MILLIONAIRE

THE QUIZ BOOK

BOXTREE

First published 1999 by Boxtree
an imprint of Macmillan Publishers Ltd
25 Eccleston Place
London SW1W 9NF
Basingstoke and Oxford

Associated companies throughout the world

www.macmillan.co.uk

ISBN 0 7522 1796 8

7 9 8

A CIP catalogue record for this book
is available from the British Library.

Designed and typeset by Blackjacks
Printed by Mackays of Chatham plc

CONTENTS

How to play

Here's the ultimate test all you armchair contestants have been waiting for – nearly a thousand teasers to test every single one of those brain cells. Picture the scene: you've won Fastest Finger First and now you're sitting in the hot-seat under the dimmed lights, ready to start your bid to climb the fifteen levels of the money tree to collect the coveted £1,000,000! You can challenge yourself, or invite some friends round and stage a tournament.

For 1 player
As on *Who Wants To Be A Millionaire?*, the aim of the game is to reach £1,000,000. Start with a question worth £100 and once you have decided on your final answer (and are absolutely sure...) follow the page reference at the foot of the page to find out if you've won that amount. If your answer is correct, you can play to win £200 and so on up the tree. The page where the £200 questions (and every other money level) begin is listed in the answer section.

As on the programme you have three lifelines to help you on your way to £1,000,000, these are, of course, optional but each of them can only be used once, so only use them when you really need to.

50:50 Fifty-Fifty
This option takes away two incorrect answers leaving the correct answer and one incorrect answer remaining, a page reference at the bottom of each page will direct you to the relevant section.

Ask the Audience

This works in exactly the same way as on *Who Wants To Be A Millionaire?* except you get to pick your audience! Wherever you are, enlist the help of as many people as you can: if you're at home, switch off the TV for a second, prize your child from the Playstation and put your family to the test. Or, if you're playing on a bus or train, call on the help of your fellow passengers – they'll probably jump at the chance to relieve the boredom of a long journey. The more people you ask, the higher your chances of choosing the correct answer. Hand around pieces of paper and give your 'audience' thirty seconds to write down what they think the answer is. Collect everybody's papers and add up how many people went for each different option. In the end, however, the final decision is yours!

Phone a Friend

If you have a telephone handy (and a willing friend!) ring him/her up to help you out. You have thirty seconds (no cheating, now...) to read the question to your friend and for them to tell you what they think the answer is. If there's someone else around, ask if they can time it for you.

If you answer incorrectly, you are out of the game. £1,000 and £32,000 are 'safe havens' so if you answer a question incorrectly and you have not reached £1,000 then not only are you out of the game but you won't have won a penny! If you have reached one (or both) of these havens and you answer a question incorrectly, then you are out of the game but you will have won the value of the previous haven you have reached. If at any point during the game you are unsure of an answer and don't want to risk losing everything if you answer incorrectly, you can 'stick' at the amount you have won so far and that will be your final score. Use the score sheets at the back of the book as you play to keep a running record of the amount you have won and the lifelines you have used.

For 2-5 players
Players should take turns at being 'Chris Tarrant' and posing questions to the other contestant/s. The rules are the same as for a single player (see above). The game is over when everyone is out or when someone wins £1,000,000... The first person to reach £1,000,000 wins the game. If no one becomes a millionaire then the player who has won the most money when everyone is out is the winner.

Are you ready to play? Good. With all that money at stake, we're sure we don't need to tell you to think very carefully before you give your final answer. Good luck and be sure to remember at all times the motto of *Who Wants To Be A Millionaire?* – it's only easy if you know the answer!

50:50

15 £1 MILLION
14 £500,000
13 £250,000
12 £125,000
11 £64,000
10 **£32,000**
9 £16,000
8 £8,000
7 £4,000
6 £2,000
5 **£1,000**
4 £500
3 £300
2 £200
1 ◆ **£100**

1 ♦ £100

1

In the Walt Disney film of the same name, what type of creature is Bambi?

- ◆A: Deer
- ◆B: Elephant
- ◆C: Mouse
- ◆D: Cat

2

Which artists won the Turner Prize in 1986?

- ◆A: Topsy and Tim
- ◆B: Gilbert and George
- ◆C: Renee and Renato
- ◆D: Little and Large

3

What does the letter E stand for in the abbreviation E-mail?

- ◆A: Easy
- ◆B: Electronic
- ◆C: European
- ◆D: Elephant

4

What name is given to people who fish with rod and line as a hobby?

- ◆A: Anglers
- ◆B: Danglers
- ◆C: Dinglers
- ◆D: Bunglers

5

The acorn is the fruit of which tree?

- ◆A: Elm
- ◆B: Oak
- ◆C: Beech
- ◆D: Shoe

If you would like to use your 50:50 please turn to page 239
Turn to the answer section on page 255 to find out if you've won £100!

6

Which of these words is slang for 'money'?

- A: Dosh
- B: Mush
- C: Kudos
- D: Hash

7

Which superhero has been portrayed on screen by Michael Keaton, Val Kilmer and George Clooney?

- A: Batman
- B: Spiderman
- C: Captain America
- D: Wonder Woman

8

With which Motown group was Diana Ross a singer in the 1960s?

- A: The Chiffons
- B: The Supremes
- C: The Ronettes
- D: The Monkees

9

What is the longest river in Italy?

- A: Po
- B: Laa-Laa
- C: Dipsy
- D: Tinky Winky

10

What kind of animal is Nipper, in the famous HMV logo?

- A: Budgerigar
- B: Piranha
- C: Giraffe
- D: Dog

If you would like to use your 50:50 please turn to page 239
Turn to the answer section on page 255 to find out if you've won £100!

11

What was the name of the banqueting hall gutted by fire at Windsor Castle in 1992?

- A: St Jason's Hall
- B: St Wayne's Hall
- C: St George's Hall
- D: St Sharon's Hall

12

Which of these diseases is transmitted to humans by the mosquito?

- A: Yellow fever
- B: Psittacosis
- C: Typhus
- D: Mumps

13

Which of the following pioneered frozen food production?

- A: Clarence Birdseye
- B: Henrik Crowsfoot
- C: Ivor Nestegg
- D: William Duckbill

14

Which city was the home town of the Beatles?

- A: Manchester
- B: Liverpool
- C: London
- D: Birmingham

15

What is the chief food of most termites?

- A: Cheese
- B: Concrete
- C: Wood
- D: Curry

If you would like to use your 50:50 please turn to page 239
Turn to the answer section on page 255 to find out if you've won £100!

16

What is the official unit of currency in Japan?

A: Ben
B: Hen
C: Yen
D: Zen

17

What name is given to the young of a kangaroo?

A: Joey
B: Jody
C: Polly
D: Bruce

18

A Mancunian is a native of which city?

A: Birmingham
B: Liverpool
C: Manchester
D: London

19

By what name was Queen Victoria's husband known?

A: Prince Victor
B: Prince Philip
C: Prince Albert
D: Prince Naseem

20

How many legs does a tripod have?

A: One
B: Three
C: Nine
D: One hundred

If you would like to use your 50:50 please turn to page 239
Turn to the answer section on page 255 to find out if you've won £100!

21

Which of these names is also a herb?

A: Rosemary | B: Beryl
C: Doris | D: Ethel

22

What kind of show did Charles Cruft establish in the 19th century?

A: Dog show | B: Boat show
C: Circus | D: Quiz show

23

Which German city is associated with a round patty of minced beef served in a bun?

A: Frankfurt | B: Hamburg
C: Bonn | D: Berlin

24

What mechanical object do the dogs chase in greyhound racing?

A: Bone | B: Hare
C: Postman | D: Steak

25

By what name is an elk known in North America?

A: Heron | B: Killer whale
C: Moose | D: Eel

If you would like to use your 50:50 please turn to page 239
Turn to the answer section on page 255 to find out if you've won £100!

26

Who quit the Spice Girls in 1998?

A: Geri

B: Victoria

C: Emma

D: Mel C

27

What is the abbreviation for the organisation founded in 1824 to enforce laws to protect animals?

A: NSPCA

B: RSPCC

C: RSPCA

D: NSPCC

28

Which type of reference book summarises items of general knowledge listed in alphabetical order?

A: Almanac

B: Thesaurus

C: Directory

D: Encyclopaedia

29

Which author created the detectives Miss Marple and Hercule Poirot?

A: Arthur Conan Doyle

B: Raymond Chandler

C: Agatha Christie

D: P.D. James

30

According to the nursery rhyme, who killed Cock Robin?

A: The wren

B: The rook

C: The thrush

D: The sparrow

If you would like to use your 50:50 please turn to page 239
Turn to the answer section on page 255 to find out if you've won £100!

31

What are the seed-bearing fruits of pine, cedar and fir trees called?

- A: Nuts
- B: Catkins
- C: Cones
- D: Gourds

32

Which spelling is correct for the word meaning 'a slight hesitation'?

- A: PORES
- B: PAWS
- C: PAUSE
- D: POURS

33

Which birds are kept in lofts and used for racing?

- A: Chickens
- B: Ducks
- C: Ostriches
- D: Pigeons

34

Andrew Lloyd Webber wrote a musical called 'The Phantom of the...' what?

- A: Opera
- B: Pantomime
- C: Ballet
- D: Mask

35

Which code helps children to cross the road?

- A: Morse code
- B: STD code
- C: Green Cross code
- D: Genetic code

If you would like to use your 50:50 please turn to page 239
Turn to the answer section on page 255 to find out if you've won £100!

36

In which of these cities could you spend pesetas?

- A: Timbuctoo
- B: Barcelona
- C: Washington DC
- D: Rome

37

Which common flower of the daisy family has a downy seed-head blown by children to tell the time?

- A: Thistle
- B: Old man's beard
- C: Knapweed
- D: Dandelion

38

As what did Sir Walter Raleigh become famous?

- A: Explorer
- B: Bicycle maker
- C: Composer
- D: Court jester

39

Who is the head of the Roman Catholic church?

- A: Pope
- B: Cardinal
- C: Shah
- D: Godfather

40

What creature appears on the flag of Wales?

- A: Sheep
- B: Duck-billed platypus
- C: Emu
- D: Dragon

If you would like to use your 50:50 please turn to page 239
Turn to the answer section on page 255 to find out if you've won £100!

41

Where might you find a tower called a keep?

A: In a castle

B: At an airport

C: On the beach

D: On a church

42

Which Australian throwing stick is supposed to return to the thrower?

A: Wallaby

B: Boomerang

C: Didgeridoo

D: Jumbuck

43

What is the shortest month of the year?

A: January

B: February

C: March

D: April

44

Which country is home to flamenco dancing?

A: Norway

B: Poland

C: Spain

D: Russia

45

What is the mathematical term for a part of a whole, such as a half or a quarter?

A: Friction

B: Fraction

C: Faction

D: Fracture

If you would like to use your 50:50 please turn to page 239
Turn to the answer section on page 255 to find out if you've won £100!

1 ◆ £100

46

Which title goes before the name
of a man who has been knighted?

A: Sir

B: Madam

C: Count

D: Prince

47

Who or what would somebody
write about in an autobiography?

A: Themself

B: A car

C: Wildlife

D: The future

48

Which form of transport moves along
on a cushion of air?

A: Monorail

B: Ferry

C: Tank

D: Hovercraft

49

Which of the following is traditionally
associated with a maypole?

A: Marriage

B: Dancing

C: Barber's shop

D: Pole-vaulting

50

Of which plant is a four-leafed
specimen considered lucky?

A: Clover

B: Cabbage

C: Willow

D: Dandelion

If you would like to use your 50:50 please turn to page 239
Turn to the answer section on page 255 to find out if you've won £100!

51

In the night sky, what can be half, full or new?

A: The Sun
B: The Moon
C: Pluto
D: Neptune

52

Which part of a book is also a type of finger?

A: Epilogue
B: Index
C: Appendix
D: Prologue

53

What name is given to the stand
on which an artist rests his canvas?

A: Pallet
B: Easel
C: Podium
D: Plinth

54

Which black and white bear-like animal lives
mainly on a diet of bamboo?

A: Zebra
B: Sheepdog
C: Skunk
D: Panda

55

To which part of the body does the word 'nasal' refer?

A: Nose
B: Heart
C: Stomach
D: Skin

If you would like to use your 50:50 please turn to page 239
Turn to the answer section on page 255 to find out if you've won £100!

56

What name is given to the liquid inside a coconut?

A: Coconut tea
B: Coconut beer
C: Cocoa
D: Coconut milk

57

Which of these people would be most likely to use a rolling pin?

A: Builder
B: Fisherman
C: Gardener
D: Baker

58

Who 'sat in the corner', according to the nursery rhyme?

A: Little Boy Blue
B: Little Jack Horner
C: Little Miss Muffet
D: Little Johnny Green

59

Which famous nurse was nicknamed 'The Lady of the Lamp'?

A: Florence Nightingale
B: Gladys Emmanuel
C: Florence Nightowl
D: Florence Nighthawk

60

From which creatures do we obtain bacon?

A: Sheep
B: Fish
C: Chickens
D: Pigs

If you would like to use your 50:50 please turn to page 239
Turn to the answer section on page 255 to find out if you've won £100!

61

On which continent is the country of South Korea?

A: Africa

B: Antarctica

C: South America

D: Asia

62

What sort of animal is Walt Disney's Dumbo?

A: Deer

B: Rabbit

C: Elephant

D: Donkey

63

According to the Bible, the infant Jesus received gifts of frankincense, myrrh and what else?

A: Rubies

B: Diamonds

C: Gold

D: Silver

64

Which political party did Margaret Thatcher lead?

A: Liberals

B: Conservatives

C: Socialist Workers

D: Monster Raving Loonies

65

Which of these mountains is the highest?

A: Everest

B: Ben Nevis

C: Mont Blanc

D: Snowdon

If you would like to use your 50:50 please turn to page 239
Turn to the answer section on page 255 to find out if you've won £100!

1 ◆ £100

66

Which group released an album called
'Sergeant Pepper's Lonely Hearts Club Band'?

A: Spice Girls

B: Oasis

C: Rolling Stones

D: Beatles

67

What is the Friday before Easter Sunday called?

A: Holy Friday

B: Maundy Friday

C: Good Friday

D: First Friday

68

What is the name of Queen Elizabeth II's husband?

A: Prince Michael

B: Prince Edinburgh

C: Prince Charming

D: Prince Philip

69

In which country did spaghetti originate?

A: France

B: Wales

C: Italy

D: Australia

70

What is a set or series of a hundred called?

A: A decade

B: A century

C: A millennium

D: A jubilee

If you would like to use your 50:50 please turn to page 239
Turn to the answer section on page 255 to find out if you've won £100!

71

What was the title of Lulu's first top ten single?

A: Shout
B: Squeak
C: Scream
D: Shriek

72

The Guinness company is famous for making which product?

A: Cars
B: Televisions
C: Beer
D: Cakes

73

In which field did Agatha Christie become famous?

A: Crime fiction
B: Dance
C: Acting
D: Wrestling

74

An admiral is a high ranking officer in which force?

A: Navy
B: Army
C: Police
D: Air force

75

Which of these best describes a cultivated mushroom?

A: Animal
B: Underwater plant
C: Edible fungus
D: Tree

If you would like to use your 50:50 please turn to page 239
Turn to the answer section on page 255 to find out if you've won £100!

76

In London, what are King's Cross,
St Pancras and Waterloo?

- A: Airports
- B: Railway stations
- C: Ferry ports
- D: Bridges

77

What is a twelfth of a foot called?

- A: A toe
- B: An inch
- C: A metre
- D: A pound

78

Where on the body should a helmet be worn?

- A: On the feet
- B: Around the waist
- C: Between the knees
- D: On the head

79

What would you usually do with an artichoke?

- A: Eat it
- B: Wear it
- C: Throw it
- D: Play it

80

How many seasons are there in a year?

- A: Four
- B: Six
- C: Twelve
- D: Twenty four

If you would like to use your 50:50 please turn to page 239
Turn to the answer section on page 255 to find out if you've won £100!

1 ◆ £100

81

Which Shakespearean character was the famous lover of Juliet?

- A: Romeo
- B: Bravo
- C: Raymond
- D: Reggie

82

In London, which river is crossed by Tower Bridge?

- A: Severn
- B: Thames
- C: Nile
- D: Seine

83

Which part of a lettuce is usually eaten in salads?

- A: Seeds
- B: Roots
- C: Berries
- D: Leaves

84

What colour ball should normally be struck by the cue in snooker?

- A: Black
- B: Mauve
- C: Orange
- D: White

85

What is another name for a moving staircase?

- A: Elevator
- B: Escalator
- C: Perambulator
- D: Rotavator

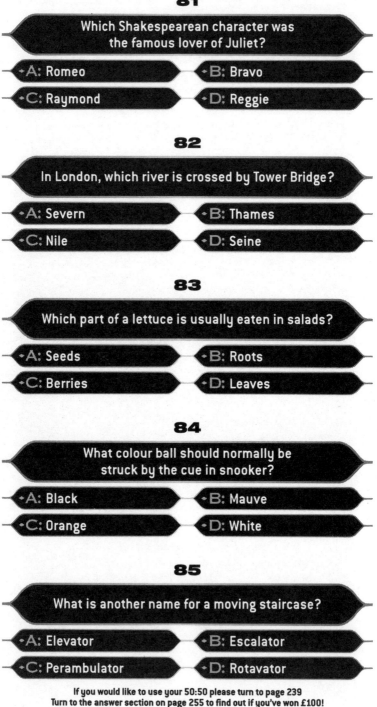

If you would like to use your 50:50 please turn to page 239
Turn to the answer section on page 255 to find out if you've won £100!

86

How would a musician play a triangle?

- A: Suck it
- B: Blow it
- C: Pluck it
- D: Strike it

87

Which of these does a horse rider sit on?

- A: Stirrup
- B: Spur
- C: Saddle
- D: Throne

88

Which fictional little girl explored Wonderland?

- A: Alice
- B: Beryl the Peril
- C: Violet Elizabeth Bott
- D: Matilda

89

What do we call the act of thumbing a lift?

- A: Hitch-hiking
- B: Camping
- C: Joyriding
- D: Orienteering

90

The United Kingdom consists of England, Wales, Northern Ireland and which other country?

- A: Turkey
- B: Iceland
- C: India
- D: Scotland

If you would like to use your 50:50 please turn to page 239
Turn to the answer section on page 255 to find out if you've won £100!

91

By what name are cinema's Academy Awards also known?

- A: Oscars
- B: Globes
- C: Emmys
- D: Tonys

92

Which hard seaside sweet is sold in sticks?

- A: Stone
- B: Cliff
- C: Rock
- D: Gravel

93

Which of the following is not the nickname of a Spice Girl?

- A: Baby Spice
- B: Scary Spice
- C: Posh Spice
- D: Saucy Spice

94

The ostrich is the largest example of which group of creatures?

- A: Birds
- B: Frogs
- C: Reptiles
- D: Insects

95

According to Benny Hill's 1971 chart topper, what was Ernie's job?

- A: Dustman
- B: Postman
- C: Milkman
- D: Solicitor

If you would like to use your 50:50 please turn to page 239
Turn to the answer section on page 255 to find out if you've won £100!

1 ◆ £100

96

Which of these is not the colour of a snooker ball?

- A: Blue
- B: Yellow
- C: Red
- D: Purple

97

Which vehicles compete in the annual Tour de France?

- A: Go-karts
- B: Cars
- C: Bicycles
- D: Tractors

98

Princess Anne has appeared on which television quiz show?

- A: Mastermind
- B: A Question of Sport
- C: Ask the Family
- D: Who Wants to Be a Millionaire?

99

What is America's theatrical equivalent of the Oscars?

- A: Tims
- B: Tonys
- C: Toms
- D: Trevors

100

What was the name of the dog owned by 'The Woodentops' in the TV series?

- A: Rover
- B: Spotty
- C: K9
- D: Fido

If you would like to use your 50:50 please turn to page 239
Turn to the answer section on page 255 to find out if you've won £100!

1 ◆ £100

101

What was the nickname of Dr McCoy from 'Star Trek'?

- A: Phones
- B: Bones
- C: Stones
- D: Jones

102

What is the main item stored in a camel's hump?

- A: Sand
- B: Pyjamas
- C: Maps
- D: Fat

103

Which of these animals does not belong to the cat family?

- A: Cheetah
- B: Leopard
- C: Rottweiler
- D: Tiger

104

Which plant is a national emblem of Scotland?

- A: Scottish heather
- B: Scots pine
- C: Scottish primrose
- D: Scotch thistle

105

Which of these is a prickly plant that usually grows in the desert?

- A: Cactus
- B: Daffodil
- C: Hyacinth
- D: Begonia

If you would like to use your 50:50 please turn to page 239
Turn to the answer section on page 255 to find out if you've won £100!

1 ◆ £100

106

Made in the Netherlands, what are Edam and Gouda?

◆A: Cheeses
◆B: Clogs
◆C: Tulips
◆D: Windmills

107

What colour is the result of mixing red and yellow?

◆A: Black
◆B: Grey
◆C: White
◆D: Orange

108

Gaelic is a type of what?

◆A: Aromatic herb
◆B: Celtic language
◆C: Swiss cheese
◆D: Egyptian writing paper

109

What would you do with a truffle?

◆A: Play it
◆B: Wear it
◆C: Spend it
◆D: Eat it

110

Which mouse does Tom the Cat chase in the famous cartoons?

◆A: Danger Mouse
◆B: Jerry Mouse
◆C: Mickey Mouse
◆D: Mighty Mouse

If you would like to use your 50:50 please turn to page 239
Turn to the answer section on page 255 to find out if you've won £100!

50:50

15	£1 MILLION
14	£500,000
13	£250,000
12	£125,000
11	£64,000
10	**£32,000**
9	£16,000
8	£8,000
7	£4,000
6	£2,000
5	**£1,000**
4	£500
3	£300
2 ◆	**£200**
1 ◆	£100

2 ◆ £200

1

According to folklore, what does
the sandman help children to do?

A: Sleep

B: Grow

C: Cross the road

D: Build sandcastles

2

In the sitcom 'Are You Being Served?',
whose catchphrase was 'I'm Free'?

A: Mr Lucas

B: Captain Peacock

C: Mrs Slocombe

D: Mr Humphries

3

During World War II, what were U-boats?

A: Aircraft carriers

B: Submarines

C: Destroyers

D: Merchant ships

4

At what weight did Frank Bruno win
a boxing world championship title?

A: Middleweight

B: Cruiserweight

C: Light-heavyweight

D: Heavyweight

5

Which word often follows 'side', 'oil' and 'ear'?

A: Drum

B: Trap

C: Car

D: Double

If you would like to use your 50:50 please turn to page 240
Turn to the answer section on page 255 to find out if you've won £200!

6

As what is saccharin mainly used?

A: Adhesive
B: Sweetener
C: Whitener
D: Solvent

7

Who starred in the films 'Saturday Night Fever' and 'Pulp Fiction'?

A: John Travolta
B: Samuel L. Jackson
C: Bruce Willis
D: Tim Roth

8

Which dance is musically associated with Matilda?

A: Tango
B: Waltz
C: Foxtrot
D: Jig

9

Who had a number one UK single with 'I Should Be So Lucky'?

A: Jason Donovan
B: Kylie Minogue
C: Dannii Minogue
D: Nick Berry

10

Which sign of the zodiac has a sting in the tail?

A: Sagittarius
B: Aries
C: Cancer
D: Scorpio

If you would like to use your 50:50 please turn to page 240
Turn to the answer section on page 255 to find out if you've won £200!

11

In which sport was Daley Thompson
an Olympic champion?

A: Cycling

B: Shooting

C: Athletics

D: Diving

12

Which word can mean to gulp down food,
to fasten or to break away?

A: Bang

B: Buck

C: Blow

D: Bolt

13

In 'The X-Files', what is Agent Mulder's first name?

A: Fox

B: Hound

C: Tiger

D: Wolf

14

Which fruit comes from bramble bushes?

A: Strawberry

B: Blackberry

C: Gooseberry

D: Cherry

15

What might be divided into stanzas?

A: Land

B: Time

C: Poetry

D: Food

If you would like to use your 50:50 please turn to page 240
Turn to the answer section on page 255 to find out if you've won £200!

16

Which country was once ruled by tsars?

A: Ireland
B: Japan
C: Russia
D: China

17

In tennis, what name is given to a service so good that the opponent fails to touch it?

A: Deuce
B: Advantage
C: Ace
D: Let

18

Which of these is a TV cop series from America?

A: NYPD Black
B: NYPD White
C: NYPD Green
D: NYPD Blue

19

What is the main characteristic of a person described as extrovert?

A: Shy
B: Clumsy
C: Greedy
D: Socially confident

20

In which country did the drink 'saki' originate?

A: Spain
B: France
C: Italy
D: Japan

If you would like to use your 50:50 please turn to page 240
Turn to the answer section on page 255 to find out if you've won £200!

21

Whose 'Thriller' album is one of the biggest selling records of all time?

◆A: Michael Jackson
◆B: Madonna
◆C: Dire Straits
◆D: Elvis Presley

22

Which popular author is the sister of Joan Collins?

◆A: Judy Collins
◆B: Jackie Collins
◆C: Jenny Collins
◆D: Jilly Collins

23

What can be 'right', 'acute' or 'reflex'?

◆A: Accent
◆B: Lens
◆C: Angle
◆D: Edge

24

Which town is famous for its salts and its racecourse?

◆A: Epsom
◆B: Ascot
◆C: Fontwell
◆D: Sandown

25

Who played the title role in the film 'Taxi Driver'?

◆A: Robert De Niro
◆B: Harvey Keitel
◆C: Al Pacino
◆D: James Caan

If you would like to use your 50:50 please turn to page 240
Turn to the answer section on page 255 to find out if you've won £200!

26

Which apparatus is used for weaving?

- A: Spinning wheel
- B: Sewing machine
- C: Loom
- D: Knitting needles

27

Who played policewoman Jane Tennison in the TV drama series 'Prime Suspect'?

- A: Amanda Burton
- B: Jill Gascoine
- C: Francesca Annis
- D: Helen Mirren

28

Which of these cities is built upon a group of islands?

- A: Madrid
- B: Paris
- C: Edinburgh
- D: Venice

29

Someone who raises false alarms is said to cry what?

- A: Fox
- B: Wolf
- C: Baby
- D: Badger

30

Which of the following is the traditional raising agent in bread?

- A: Flour
- B: Eggs
- C: Hops
- D: Yeast

If you would like to use your 50:50 please turn to page 240
Turn to the answer section on page 255 to find out if you've won £200!

31

Who sang about being a 'Private Dancer' in the 1984 singles chart?

A: Belinda Carlisle
B: Tina Turner
C: Whitney Houston
D: Madonna

32

In England and Wales, which of the following is usually made up of twelve people?

A: Football team
B: Wind quartet
C: Jury
D: Tug-of-war team

33

Which word means an accidental success?

A: Fluke
B: Fluff
C: Flop
D: Flute

34

On television, which of these pubs is in Walford?

A: The Rover's Return
B: The Woolpack
C: The Nag's Head
D: The Queen Victoria

35

For which country does footballer Michael Owen play?

A: England
B: Wales
C: Scotland
D: Northern Ireland

If you would like to use your 50:50 please turn to page 240
Turn to the answer section on page 255 to find out if you've won £200!

36

What is the correct term for the rotating part of a windmill?

A: Sails

B: Propellers

C: Spinners

D: Wings

37

How were Bill Oddie, Graeme Garden and Tim Brooke-Taylor better known in a TV comedy series?

A: Goodies

B: Three of a Kind

C: Three Stooges

D: Young Ones

38

Around which part of the body would you wear a dicky bow?

A: Waist

B: Ankle

C: Wrist

D: Neck

39

What is the opposite of 'temporary'?

A: Residential

B: Permanent

C: Infinite

D: Makeshift

40

Which wooded area of Nottinghamshire was originally a royal park where medieval kings hunted deer?

A: Forest of Arden

B: Sherwood Forest

C: New Forest

D: Epping Forest

If you would like to use your 50:50 please turn to page 240
Turn to the answer section on page 255 to find out if you've won £200!

2 ◆ £200

41

To what did the singer Charles Berry change his first name?

- A: Chuck
- B: Dave
- C: Cliff
- D: Hank

42

Which of these TV-based movies starred Tom Cruise?

- A: Lost in Space
- B: The Saint
- C: Mission Impossible
- D: The Fugitive

43

What name is given to wool immediately after it is removed from a sheep?

- A: Pelt
- B: Hide
- C: Fleece
- D: Down

44

What would you use to play a game of 'rummy'?

- A: Coins
- B: Cards
- C: Dice
- D: Dominoes

45

Which country's flag has a maple leaf in the centre?

- A: France
- B: Ireland
- C: Australia
- D: Canada

If you would like to use your 50:50 please turn to page 240
Turn to the answer section on page 255 to find out if you've won £200!

46

What was J.R.'s surname in the TV soap 'Dallas'?

- A: Barnes
- B: Harper
- C: Colby
- D: Ewing

47

According to the famous proverb, where should you not 'look a gift horse'?

- A: In the eyes
- B: In the mouth
- C: On the hoof
- D: Between the ears

48

To which of these products is fluoride commonly added?

- A: Shampoo
- B: Oven cleaner
- C: Toothpaste
- D: Soap

49

Near which city did Euro Disney open in 1992?

- A: Berlin
- B: Rome
- C: Madrid
- D: Paris

50

Chapatis come from the cuisine of which country?

- A: China
- B: Italy
- C: France
- D: India

If you would like to use your 50:50 please turn to page 240
Turn to the answer section on page 255 to find out if you've won £200!

51

Which allergy to pollen affects many people during the summer?

- A: Shingles
- B: Hay fever
- C: Prickly heat
- D: Migraine

52

Who told his 'Angels' what to do in a popular American TV series?

- A: Freddie
- B: Charlie
- C: Alfie
- D: Frankie

53

What sort of travel is associated with Cape Canaveral?

- A: Space travel
- B: Sea travel
- C: Rail travel
- D: Road travel

54

In which game do players try to reduce their score to zero?

- A: Snooker
- B: Rugby
- C: Darts
- D: Bowls

55

'AD' after a date signifies a number of years after the birth of whom?

- A: Adam
- B: God
- C: Moses
- D: Jesus Christ

If you would like to use your 50:50 please turn to page 240
Turn to the answer section on page 255 to find out if you've won £200!

56

Which of these films featured a lovable visitor from space?

- A: Alien
- B: Armageddon
- C: E.T. The Extra-Terrestrial
- D: Independence Day

57

Which food is made from ground almonds, sugar and egg whites?

- A: Marzipan
- B: Marmite
- C: Marjoram
- D: Marmalade

58

Which animal is associated with the beginning of an MGM film?

- A: Tiger
- B: Bear
- C: Unicorn
- D: Lion

59

Which of the following is a large stone circle on Salisbury Plain?

- A: Hadrian's Wall
- B: Stonehenge
- C: Salisbury Cathedral
- D: The Old Man of Hoy

60

What is the alternative name for Holland?

- A: The Nether Regions
- B: The Lowlands
- C: The Netherlands
- D: Benelux

If you would like to use your 50:50 please turn to page 240
Turn to the answer section on page 255 to find out if you've won £200!

61

By what name was the fashion designer Gabrielle Chanel known?

- A: Coco
- B: Jojo
- C: Dodo
- D: Yoyo

62

Which country was the setting for the TV series 'The Waltons'?

- A: USA
- B: Scotland
- C: New Zealand
- D: Australia

63

Which form of painting would show a traditional view of the countryside?

- A: Portrait
- B: Still Life
- C: Abstract
- D: Landscape

64

What type of flag is shown to the winner of a Grand Prix motor race?

- A: Yellow
- B: Union Jack
- C: Chequered
- D: Striped

65

Which four letters commonly go before both 'vision' and 'phone' to make two new words?

- A: Info
- B: Xylo
- C: Tele
- D: Gram

If you would like to use your 50:50 please turn to page 240
Turn to the answer section on page 255 to find out if you've won £200!

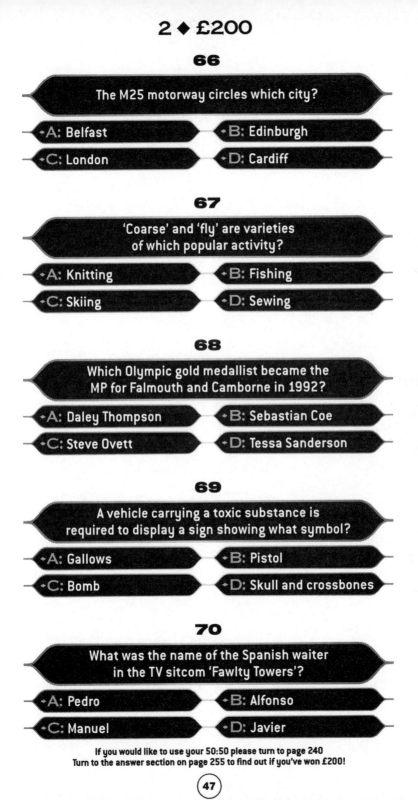

66

The M25 motorway circles which city?

A: Belfast

B: Edinburgh

C: London

D: Cardiff

67

'Coarse' and 'fly' are varieties
of which popular activity?

A: Knitting

B: Fishing

C: Skiing

D: Sewing

68

Which Olympic gold medallist became the
MP for Falmouth and Camborne in 1992?

A: Daley Thompson

B: Sebastian Coe

C: Steve Ovett

D: Tessa Sanderson

69

A vehicle carrying a toxic substance is
required to display a sign showing what symbol?

A: Gallows

B: Pistol

C: Bomb

D: Skull and crossbones

70

What was the name of the Spanish waiter
in the TV sitcom 'Fawlty Towers'?

A: Pedro

B: Alfonso

C: Manuel

D: Javier

If you would like to use your 50:50 please turn to page 240
Turn to the answer section on page 255 to find out if you've won £200!

71

To which country does the island of Crete belong?

A: Italy

B: Greece

C: Turkey

D: Spain

72

How many points is the outer bull's-eye worth in darts?

A: 20

B: 25

C: 40

D: 50

73

Which type of instrument is a trombone?

A: Brass

B: Woodwind

C: String

D: Percussion

74

In their chart-topping football anthem, David Baddiel and Frank Skinner sang about 'Three...' what?

A: Lions

B: Goals

C: Chances

D: Penalties

75

Where on the body is the nape?

A: Leg

B: Chest

C: Arm

D: Neck

If you would like to use your 50:50 please turn to page 240
Turn to the answer section on page 255 to find out if you've won £200!

76

What is the name of the enclosed platform in a church from which a sermon is delivered?

A: Pulpit | B: Nave
C: Altar | D: Transept

77

Which American university shares its name with a kind of lock?

A: Princeton | B: Stanford
C: Yale | D: Harvard

78

Which word can follow 'conger' and 'electric'?

A: Shark | B: Snake
C: Eel | D: Lamprey

79

Who played Hannibal Lecter in the film 'The Silence of the Lambs'?

A: Bob Hoskins | B: Jeremy Irons
C: Pierce Brosnan | D: Anthony Hopkins

80

Which emperor built a famous wall to limit incursions of Northern tribes into Roman England?

A: Hadrian | B: Julius Caesar
C: Nero | D: Claudius

If you would like to use your 50:50 please turn to page 240
Turn to the answer section on page 255 to find out if you've won £200!

81

What is a hydrofoil?

- A: Sea vessel
- B: Aeroplane
- C: Racing car
- D: Space rocket

82

Who stands in the dock during a criminal trial?

- A: Judge
- B: Accused
- C: Jury
- D: Lawyers

83

Where would you wear galoshes?

- A: On the head
- B: On the hands
- C: On the feet
- D: Around the waist

84

Which bloodsucking creatures were once commonly used by doctors?

- A: Vampire bats
- B: Leeches
- C: Mosquitoes
- D: Snakes

85

What sort of food is a bagel?

- A: Fruit
- B: Bread roll
- C: Sausage
- D: Fish

If you would like to use your 50:50 please turn to page 240
Turn to the answer section on page 255 to find out if you've won £200!

86

Which group sang about 'Shiny Happy People' in 1991?

A: REM

B: Talking Heads

C: The Wonder Stuff

D: Erasure

87

In 1996, Leonardo DiCaprio starred in a film version of which Shakespeare play?

A: Hamlet

B: Twelfth Night

C: Romeo and Juliet

D: Much Ado About Nothing

88

What does 'surly' mean?

A: Certainly

B: Over

C: Bad-tempered

D: Dirty

89

Which of these abbreviations might you find on a carton of milk?

A: UHT

B: FHM

C: VHF

D: WHO

90

On what surface does a toboggan usually travel?

A: Grass

B: Sand

C: Water

D: Snow

If you would like to use your 50:50 please turn to page 240
Turn to the answer section on page 255 to find out if you've won £200!

91

Which surname connects movie stars Henry, Peter, Jane and Bridget?

A: Barrymore
B: Fonda
C: Russell
D: Ford

92

In which city is the Empire State Building?

A: Chicago
B: Washington DC
C: Miami
D: New York

93

'I Like It' was a massive hit for 1960s pop group 'Gerry and the...' who?

A: Dreamers
B: Comets
C: Pacemakers
D: Crickets

94

The island of Tasmania is part of which country?

A: Brazil
B: New Zealand
C: Indonesia
D: Australia

95

What is a klaxon?

A: Character in 'Star Trek'
B: Loud hooter
C: German cake
D: Sub-atomic particle

If you would like to use your 50:50 please turn to page 240
Turn to the answer section on page 255 to find out if you've won £200!

96

Which word means a signed document in support of a particular action?

A: Partition

B: Position

C: Perforation

D: Petition

97

Which of these is set in rural Ambridge?

A: Emmerdale

B: The Archers

C: Hollyoaks

D: Family Affairs

98

What name is given to scribblings or drawings on public walls?

A: Plasterwork

B: Graphicacy

C: Pointing

D: Graffiti

If you would like to use your 50:50 please turn to page 240
Turn to the answer section on page 255 to find out if you've won £200!

1

What do you do if you 'grease someone's palm'?

A: Tell a fortune
B: Bribe someone
C: Give a warning
D: Shake hands

2

What is the sum of the interior angles of a triangle?

A: 360 degrees
B: 90 degrees
C: 180 degrees
D: 3 degrees

3

The flowers of the common forsythia shrub are normally what colour?

A: Red
B: Blue
C: Yellow
D: Purple

4

Which classic serial starred Jeremy Irons and Anthony Andrews?

A: Jewel In The Crown
B: The Far Pavilions
C: Brideshead Revisited
D: The Forsyte Saga

5

Which city replaced Calcutta as India's capital in 1912?

A: Delhi
B: Bombay
C: Colombo
D: Madras

If you would like to use your 50:50 please turn to page 242
Turn to the answer section on page 256 to find out if you've won £300!

6

What nationality is the Formula One racing driver Mika Hakkinen?

- A: Norwegian
- B: Swedish
- C: Danish
- D: Finnish

7

What is a yak?

- A: Sweet potato
- B: Muslim veil
- C: Boat
- D: Long-haired Tibetan ox

8

What is the surname of the brothers who make up the Bee Gees?

- A: Gibb
- B: Gates
- C: Gilbert
- D: Gallagher

9

Where was the new Scottish Parliament opened in 1999?

- A: Edinburgh
- B: Aberdeen
- C: Dunfermline
- D: Brighton

10

Who invented psychoanalysis?

- A: Lucien Freud
- B: Clement Freud
- C: Emma Freud
- D: Sigmund Freud

If you would like to use your 50:50 please turn to page 242
Turn to the answer section on page 256 to find out if you've won £300!

3 ◆ £300

11

For which national Rugby Union side has Gavin Hastings been a record scorer?

- A: Scotland
- B: Ireland
- C: Wales
- D: England

12

Which fictional area is the setting for 'The Bill'?

- A: Walford
- B: Erinsborough
- C: Sun Hill
- D: Cardale

13

In the USA, what are Yellowstone and Yosemite?

- A: Great Lakes
- B: Ivy League Colleges
- C: New York Boroughs
- D: National Parks

14

What is the technical term for the main body of an aeroplane?

- A: Cockpit
- B: Aileron
- C: Fuselage
- D: Aerofoil

15

Which of these bears is native to South America?

- A: Spectacled bear
- B: Gloved bear
- C: Wigged bear
- D: Raincoated bear

If you would like to use your 50:50 please turn to page 242
Turn to the answer section on page 256 to find out if you've won £300!

3 ◆ £300

16

Which first name goes before Bull, Dory and o'Groats?

- A: Jim
- B: Jack
- C: John
- D: Jane

17

As what was Liberace famous?

- A: Bullfighter
- B: Pianist
- C: Footballer
- D: Soldier

18

Who played the title role in the epic film 'Lawrence of Arabia'?

- A: Richard Harris
- B: Alec Guinness
- C: Richard Attenborough
- D: Peter O'Toole

19

Glucose is a form of which substance?

- A: Salt
- B: Sugar
- C: Acid
- D: Oil

20

When eaten, which part of a cow is known as tripe?

- A: Tongue
- B: Rump
- C: Neck
- D: Stomach lining

If you would like to use your 50:50 please turn to page 242
Turn to the answer section on page 256 to find out if you've won £300!

21

Which fictional resort is terrorised by
a great white shark in the film 'Jaws'?

A: Long Beach
B: Bodega Bay
C: Newport News
D: Amity Island

22

What nickname is traditionally given
to the clubhouse bar on a golf course?

A: 10th hole
B: 14th hole
C: 18th hole
D: 19th hole

23

Who won the 1967 Eurovision Song Contest
with 'Puppet on a String'?

A: Cilla Black
B: Petula Clark
C: Marianne Faithfull
D: Sandie Shaw

24

What name is given to the path of
one body in space around another?

A: Ambit
B: Orbit
C: Gambit
D: Audit

25

Pyrotechnics means a display of what?

A: Aircraft
B: Fireworks
C: Acrobats
D: Animals

If you would like to use your 50:50 please turn to page 242
Turn to the answer section on page 256 to find out if you've won £300!

26

Where is the Yukon river?

A: Europe
B: Asia
C: Africa
D: North America

27

Which tool is used for spreading mortar?

A: Mattock
B: Hoe
C: Trowel
D: Spade

28

Which of these words can go before 'pond', 'tail' and 'hook'?

A: Duck
B: Mill
C: Fish
D: Boat

29

What is Perry Mason's occupation in the TV series?

A: Doctor
B: Lawyer
C: Writer
D: Policeman

30

What does 'ambience' mean?

A: Unhappiness
B: Atmosphere
C: Indifference
D: Nutrition

If you would like to use your 50:50 please turn to page 242
Turn to the answer section on page 256 to find out if you've won £300!

31

Which group was led by Bryan Ferry in the 1970s?

- A: Dire Straits
- B: Pink Floyd
- C: Roxy Music
- D: The Faces

32

What is a damson?

- A: Woman in distress
- B: Fruit
- C: Carriage
- D: Musical instrument

33

Which shoes were first worn by North American Indians?

- A: Clogs
- B: Sabots
- C: Sandals
- D: Moccasins

34

What sort of race was athlete Sebastian Coe's speciality?

- A: Sprint
- B: Middle distance
- C: Hurdles
- D: Marathon

35

Historically, which of these was particularly associated with the cavalry?

- A: Parachutes
- B: Tanks
- C: Cannons
- D: Horses

If you would like to use your 50:50 please turn to page 242
Turn to the answer section on page 256 to find out if you've won £300!

36

Which word commonly goes before 'foot', 'back' and 'faced' to make three new words?

- A: Black
- B: Big
- C: Bare
- D: Broad

37

What was Sarah, Duchess of York's maiden name?

- A: Phillips
- B: Cavendish
- C: Rhys-Jones
- D: Ferguson

38

Which of these countries is made up entirely of islands?

- A: China
- B: Japan
- C: Portugal
- D: Greece

39

Which word commonly goes before 'delight' and 'bath'?

- A: Dutch
- B: Greek
- C: Turkish
- D: Romanian

40

Which musical features the songs 'I Feel Pretty' and 'Tonight'?

- A: West Side Story
- B: My Fair Lady
- C: Carousel
- D: Guys and Dolls

If you would like to use your 50:50 please turn to page 242
Turn to the answer section on page 256 to find out if you've won £300!

41

What was the principal language of ancient Rome?

A: Ancient Greek
B: Latin
C: Persian
D: Armenian

42

Which stone is also the name of a small round ball of glass?

A: Basalt
B: Granite
C: Limestone
D: Marble

43

Who is Ryan O'Neal's Oscar-winning daughter?

A: Shirley
B: Tatum
C: Bridget
D: Carrie

44

In which city is the TV soap 'Brookside' set?

A: London
B: Liverpool
C: Manchester
D: Birmingham

45

What is the collective term for the group of directors who run a large company?

A: Council
B: Cabinet
C: Board
D: Panel

If you would like to use your 50:50 please turn to page 242
Turn to the answer section on page 256 to find out if you've won £300!

46

Natural rubber usually comes from which source?

A: Trees

B: Coal

C: Oil

D: Clay

47

What does the letter P stand for in the abbreviation OAP?

A: Public

B: Pensioner

C: Person

D: Parent

48

How many hours from Tulsa was Gene Pitney in his 1963 hit song?

A: 12

B: 24

C: 36

D: 48

49

Which country was called Siam until 1939?

A: Burma

B: Thailand

C: Vietnam

D: Taiwan

50

The headstreams and waters of which river drain half the South American continent?

A: Orinoco

B: Paraguay

C: Amazon

D: Limpopo

If you would like to use your 50:50 please turn to page 242
Turn to the answer section on page 256 to find out if you've won £300!

51

In the well known phrases, if Grace is Amazing and Polly is Pretty, what is Lizzie?

- A: Dizzy
- B: Dozy
- C: Busy
- D: Lazy

52

In the UK, what do the initials HST stand for?

- A: Health Service Trust
- B: Highways Safety Tribunal
- C: High Speed Train
- D: Horizontal Screen Television

53

Who sang 'I Will Always Love You' on the soundtrack of the film 'The Bodyguard'?

- A: Whitney Houston
- B: Mariah Carey
- C: Gladys Knight
- D: Diana Ross

54

Which of these sports is most associated with Badminton House?

- A: Shooting
- B: Three-day eventing
- C: Squash
- D: Archery

55

Which battles took place between the Royal Houses of York and Lancaster?

- A: Thirty Years War
- B: Hundred Years War
- C: Wars Of The Roses
- D: English Civil War

If you would like to use your 50:50 please turn to page 242
Turn to the answer section on page 256 to find out if you've won £300!

56

Which term is used to describe a very good investment?

A: Potato chip

B: Wood chip

C: Green chip

D: Blue chip

57

In which field did John Constable become famous?

A: Art

B: Fashion

C: Literature

D: Politics

58

What is a mamba?

A: Dance

B: Snake

C: Fruit

D: Mammal

59

What does the letter L stand
for in the abbreviation 'SWALK'?

A: Little

B: Loving

C: Lingering

D: Long

60

The substance used to make casts
is known as 'Plaster of...' what?

A: Brussels

B: Prague

C: Marseilles

D: Paris

If you would like to use your 50:50 please turn to page 242
Turn to the answer section on page 256 to find out if you've won £300!

61

What was the occupation of the man commemorated by Scots on Burns Night?

- A: Soldier
- B: Explorer
- C: Poet
- D: Clan chieftain

62

Diana Ross topped the singles charts in 1986 with her 'Chain...' what?

- A: Letter
- B: Gang
- C: Mail
- D: Reaction

63

What is a 'labyrinth'?

- A: Maze
- B: Flower
- C: Research centre
- D: Vegetable

64

In which field of the arts was Rudolf Nureyev a leading figure?

- A: Sculpture
- B: Ballet
- C: Photography
- D: Opera

65

Which country is nearest to the island of Jersey?

- A: England
- B: Ireland
- C: Spain
- D: France

If you would like to use your 50:50 please turn to page 242
Turn to the answer section on page 256 to find out if you've won £300!

66

Which TV doctor was played by Sylvester McCoy?

A: Dr Kildare B: Dr Finlay

C: Dr Who D: Dr McCoy

67

What is at the centre of the Solar System?

A: Moon B: Sun

C: Earth D: Mercury

68

What type of music is 'plainsong'?

A: Rap B: Jazz

C: Church music D: Country and Western

69

On which continent are the five 'Great Lakes'?

A: Europe B: Australia

C: Africa D: North America

70

What sort of race is the highlight of the film 'Ben Hur'?

A: Steeplechase B: Chariot race

C: Marathon D: Boat race

If you would like to use your 50:50 please turn to page 242
Turn to the answer section on page 256 to find out if you've won £300!

71

Which TV series featured Florence, Dougal and Zebedee?

- A: The Magic Roundabout
- B: The Wombles
- C: The Clangers
- D: Rugrats

72

In the USA, what was outlawed by 'Prohibition'?

- A: Gambling
- B: Drinking alcohol
- C: Smoking
- D: Slavery

73

How many lines are there in a limerick?

- A: 2
- B: 4
- C: 5
- D: 8

74

What is Britain's highest military award for bravery?

- A: OBE
- B: Victoria Cross
- C: Purple Heart
- D: Silver Star

75

Which musical features the song 'Don't Cry For Me Argentina'?

- A: Cats
- B: Evita
- C: Starlight Express
- D: Sunset Boulevard

If you would like to use your 50:50 please turn to page 242
Turn to the answer section on page 256 to find out if you've won £300!

76

In which film does Dooley Wilson
sing 'As Time Goes By'?

A: The Maltese Falcon   B: Casablanca

C: The African Queen   D: The Big Sleep

77

What did the Scottish inventor
James Watt help to develop?

A: Steam engine   B: Spinning wheel

C: Radio   D: Motor car

78

Which flowers were the subject of several
famous paintings by Vincent van Gogh?

A: Venus flytraps   B: Sunflowers

C: Snapdragons   D: Daffodils

79

What was the vegetable booby prize in the
'Double or Drop' game on TV's 'Crackerjack'?

A: Cauliflower   B: Marrow

C: Cabbage   D: Turnip

80

Which famous mountain overlooks Rio de Janeiro?

A: Sugar Loaf   B: Currant Bun

C: Sponge Finger   D: Fairy Cake

If you would like to use your 50:50 please turn to page 242
Turn to the answer section on page 256 to find out if you've won £300!

81

Which flower provided Vince Hill
with the title of a 1967 hit single?

- A: Daisy
- B: Edelweiss
- C: Daffodil
- D: Pansy

82

Between 1577 and 1580, who captained
a ship called the Golden Hind?

- A: Francis Drake
- B: Christopher Columbus
- C: Roald Amundsen
- D: Charles Darwin

83

Which of these television series
featured Kermit the Frog?

- A: The Woodentops
- B: The Munsters
- C: The Muppet Show
- D: Tales of the Riverbank

84

In which craft would you make use of a kiln?

- A: Pottery
- B: Basket weaving
- C: Rug making
- D: Wood carving

85

In which sport is Steven Redgrave
an Olympic medallist?

- A: Swimming
- B: Shooting
- C: Cycling
- D: Rowing

If you would like to use your 50:50 please turn to page 242
Turn to the answer section on page 256 to find out if you've won £300!

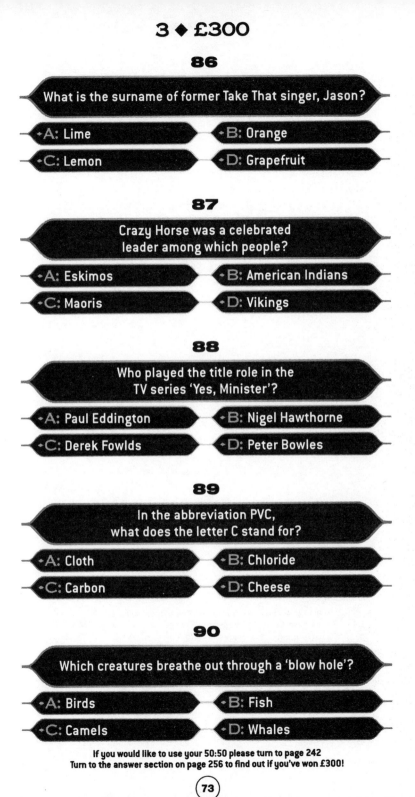

86

What is the surname of former Take That singer, Jason?

A: Lime

B: Orange

C: Lemon

D: Grapefruit

87

Crazy Horse was a celebrated leader among which people?

A: Eskimos

B: American Indians

C: Maoris

D: Vikings

88

Who played the title role in the TV series 'Yes, Minister'?

A: Paul Eddington

B: Nigel Hawthorne

C: Derek Fowlds

D: Peter Bowles

89

In the abbreviation PVC, what does the letter C stand for?

A: Cloth

B: Chloride

C: Carbon

D: Cheese

90

Which creatures breathe out through a 'blow hole'?

A: Birds

B: Fish

C: Camels

D: Whales

If you would like to use your 50:50 please turn to page 242
Turn to the answer section on page 256 to find out if you've won £300!

91

Tommy and Bobby are the
first names of which TV comedy duo?

A: Reeves and Mortimer

B: Cannon and Ball

C: Hale and Pace

D: Little and Large

92

What was the surname of the brothers
who built the first hot-air balloon?

A: Bleriot

B: Wright

C: Montgolfier

D: Eyre-Bourne

93

In which sport did Mark Spitz win a record
seven gold medals at the 1972 Olympics?

A: Skiing

B: Weightlifting

C: Gymnastics

D: Swimming

94

Which actor had a surprise
chart-topper with 'If' in 1975?

A: James Garner

B: Lee Marvin

C: Telly Savalas

D: David Soul

If you would like to use your 50:50 please turn to page 242
Turn to the answer section on page 256 to find out if you've won £300!

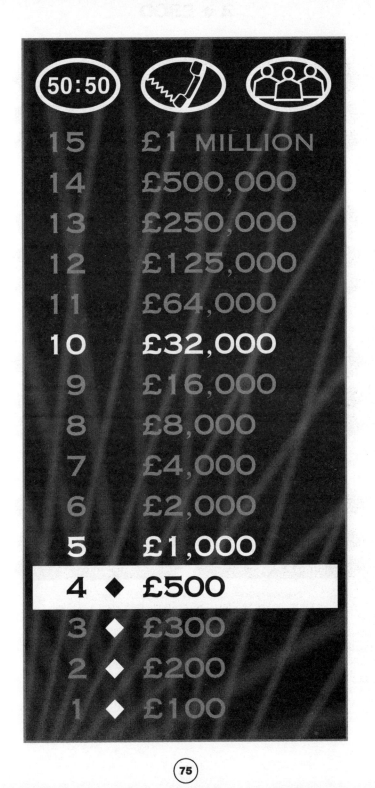

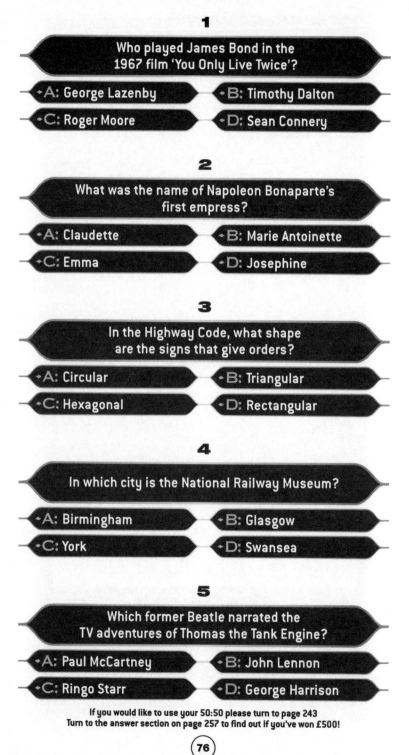

1

Who played James Bond in the
1967 film 'You Only Live Twice'?

A: George Lazenby

B: Timothy Dalton

C: Roger Moore

D: Sean Connery

2

What was the name of Napoleon Bonaparte's
first empress?

A: Claudette

B: Marie Antoinette

C: Emma

D: Josephine

3

In the Highway Code, what shape
are the signs that give orders?

A: Circular

B: Triangular

C: Hexagonal

D: Rectangular

4

In which city is the National Railway Museum?

A: Birmingham

B: Glasgow

C: York

D: Swansea

5

Which former Beatle narrated the
TV adventures of Thomas the Tank Engine?

A: Paul McCartney

B: John Lennon

C: Ringo Starr

D: George Harrison

If you would like to use your 50:50 please turn to page 243
Turn to the answer section on page 257 to find out if you've won £500!

6

Who played fictional movie star Anna Scott in the film 'Notting Hill'?

A: Andie MacDowell
B: Sandra Bullock
C: Julia Roberts
D: Cameron Diaz

7

Who became British prime minister in 1970?

A: Edward Heath
B: John Major
C: Margaret Thatcher
D: Tony Blair

8

In which city is the permanent home of the Bolshoi Ballet?

A: Moscow
B: New York
C: Milan
D: Paris

9

What was the first name of President Mitterand of France?

A: Jacques
B: Charles
C: Francois
D: Edouard

10

In which sport is the herringbone technique used for going uphill?

A: Skiing
B: Rock climbing
C: Mountain biking
D: Hang gliding

If you would like to use your 50:50 please turn to page 243
Turn to the answer section on page 257 to find out if you've won £500!

4 ◆ £500

11

In which sport would you use a pommel horse?

- A: Showjumping
- B: Fencing
- C: Gymnastics
- D: Snooker

12

How many Academy Awards did the 1997 film 'Titanic' receive?

- A: 1
- B: 2
- C: 4
- D: 11

13

What word describes a person who illegally gains access to private computer systems using a PC?

- A: Surfer
- B: Hacker
- C: Looker
- D: Tracker

14

Which Royal couple have a London museum named after them?

- A: Victoria and Albert
- B: Elizabeth and Philip
- C: William and Mary
- D: Henry and Eleanor

15

Which football manager lifted the FA Cup in May 1997?

- A: Arsene Wenger
- B: Alex Ferguson
- C: Kevin Keegan
- D: Ruud Gullit

If you would like to use your 50:50 please turn to page 243
Turn to the answer section on page 257 to find out if you've won £500!

16

Who co-wrote the song 'Do They Know It's Christmas' with Bob Geldof?

- A: David Bowie
- B: Midge Ure
- C: Phil Collins
- D: Paul McCartney

17

Gordon Sumner is the real name of which pop star?

- A: Meat Loaf
- B: Seal
- C: Sting
- D: Fish

18

In which month is the Chelsea Flower Show held each year?

- A: January
- B: May
- C: October
- D: December

19

What does the Latin word 'circa' mean when written before a year?

- A: Until
- B: Born in
- C: Around
- D: After

20

In which part of the world is the 'limbo' a local dance?

- A: Hawaii
- B: East Africa
- C: West Indies
- D: Indonesia

If you would like to use your 50:50 please turn to page 243
Turn to the answer section on page 257 to find out if you've won £500!

4 ◆ £500

21

Which of these words is Australian slang for a friend?

- A: Cobber
- B: Digger
- C: Drongo
- D: Galah

22

Who starred as Fanny Brice in the film musical 'Funny Girl'?

- A: Julie Andrews
- B: Twiggy
- C: Audrey Hepburn
- D: Barbra Streisand

23

What nickname was given to the stock market crash that began on 19th October 1987?

- A: Black Monday
- B: Black Wednesday
- C: Black Thursday
- D: Black Friday

24

Which part of the body would be affected by 'astigmatism'?

- A: Heart
- B: Eyes
- C: Lungs
- D: Hips

25

What gives the Greek spirit ouzo its flavour?

- A: Aubergine
- B: Cheese
- C: Tobacco
- D: Aniseed

If you would like to use your 50:50 please turn to page 243
Turn to the answer section on page 257 to find out if you've won £500!

26

What was first seen on British television in 1982?

A: Channel 4

B: Teletubbies

C: BBC 2

D: Coronation Street

27

In the Bible, who led the Children of Israel out of Egypt to the Promised Land?

A: David

B: Moses

C: Jacob

D: Isaac

28

What was Madonna's first single to enter the UK singles chart?

A: Holiday

B: Vogue

C: Frozen

D: Erotica

29

Which of these is a water ice of fruit juice?

A: Fool

B: Sorbet

C: Syllabub

D: Junket

30

Which sign of the zodiac is represented by a ram?

A: Aquarius

B: Capricorn

C: Taurus

D: Aries

If you would like to use your 50:50 please turn to page 243
Turn to the answer section on page 257 to find out if you've won £500!

31

Who was Danger Mouse's sidekick?

- A: Penfold
- B: Billfold
- C: Paperfold
- D: Scaffold

32

Which other fruit does a plantain resemble in shape?

- A: Banana
- B: Star fruit
- C: Strawberry
- D: Passion fruit

33

In which TV series was the phrase 'I have a cunning plan' often heard?

- A: Minder
- B: Blackadder
- C: Only Fools and Horses
- D: The Young Ones

34

Which of these is both a Beatles hit single and a street in Liverpool?

- A: Abbey Road
- B: Penny Lane
- C: Blue Jay Way
- D: Electric Avenue

35

What name is given to the tracks on which tanks and bulldozers run?

- A: Caterpillar
- B: Centipede
- C: Inchworm
- D: Snail

If you would like to use your 50:50 please turn to page 243
Turn to the answer section on page 257 to find out if you've won £500!

36

In the Bible, who was killed by Cain?

A: Noah

B: Aaron

C: Abel

D: Moses

37

In which field was John Betjeman famous?

A: Music

B: Poetry

C: Cricket

D: Photography

38

'Diaper' is the North American term for what?

A: Scarf

B: Nappy

C: Tap

D: Jumper

39

What nationality was shared
by the composers Vivaldi and Verdi?

A: Swedish

B: Italian

C: French

D: German

40

What was the name of the little girl who
owned Bagpuss in the children's TV series?

A: Courtney

B: Tiffany

C: Kylie

D: Emily

If you would like to use your 50:50 please turn to page 243
Turn to the answer section on page 257 to find out if you've won £500!

4 ◆ £500

41

Which of these drinks originated in Mexico?

A: Tequila

B: Sherry

C: Bourbon

D: Saki

42

When written down, which punctuation mark follows a command, or a shout of surprise?

A: Semi-colon

B: Exclamation mark

C: Inverted commas

D: Question mark

43

Which Shakespeare play was adapted into the hit musical 'West Side Story'?

A: The Taming of the Shrew

B: Romeo and Juliet

C: The Two Gentlemen of Verona

D: Much Ado About Nothing

44

Which of these colours does not appear on the Italian flag?

A: Red

B: Grey

C: Green

D: White

45

What type of animal is the North American roadrunner?

A: Rodent

B: Snake

C: Lizard

D: Bird

If you would like to use your 50:50 please turn to page 243
Turn to the answer section on page 257 to find out if you've won £500!

46

Which English king supposedly burnt the cakes?

- A: Harold
- B: Canute
- C: Alfred
- D: Ethelred

47

Which of these amounts is equal to a gross?

- A: Three score
- B: A ton and a half
- C: A dozen dozen
- D: Half a monkey

48

Who or what is a vegan?

- A: Native of Las Vegas
- B: Alien
- C: Strict vegetarian
- D: Plant

49

Which king gave his name to a type of spaniel?

- A: Charles I
- B: Charles II
- C: Richard III
- D: George IV

50

What type of creature was Dylan in TV's 'The Magic Roundabout'?

- A: Tortoise
- B: Rabbit
- C: Cow
- D: Snail

If you would like to use your 50:50 please turn to page 243
Turn to the answer section on page 257 to find out if you've won £500!

4 ◆ £500

51

According to tradition, what provided a hiding place for King Charles II after the Battle of Worcester?

A: Cave
B: Oak tree
C: Church
D: Pub

52

In which city can you board a train at Waverley Station?

A: Belfast
B: Cardiff
C: Bristol
D: Edinburgh

53

In which country is the wine Liebfraumilch produced?

A: Austria
B: France
C: Germany
D: South Africa

54

Which popular hobby is also known as 'ornithology'?

A: Dressmaking
B: Birdwatching
C: Seafishing
D: Clockwatching

55

Who was the original host of TV's 'Family Fortunes'?

A: Bob Monkhouse
B: Max Bygraves
C: Les Dennis
D: Bruce Forsyth

If you would like to use your 50:50 please turn to page 243
Turn to the answer section on page 257 to find out if you've won £500!

56

If you ordered 'grenouilles' in a French restaurant, what would you be served?

A: Bread

B: Frogs' legs

C: Wine

D: Onions

57

What was the title of Shakin' Stevens' hit which topped the charts in 1981?

A: Yellow Window

B: Green Door

C: Blue Room

D: Red Roof

58

Which horse won the Grand National three times?

A: Red Rum

B: Mr Frisk

C: The Colonel

D: West Tip

59

What is Frasier's surname in the TV sitcom?

A: Peacock

B: Crane

C: Stork

D: Heron

60

What relation is the Princess Royal to Princess Beatrice?

A: Cousin

B: Grandmother

C: Aunt

D: Stepmother

If you would like to use your 50:50 please turn to page 243
Turn to the answer section on page 257 to find out if you've won £500!

4 ◆ £500

61

Which Dickens character teaches
Oliver Twist how to pick pockets?

A: Bob Cratchit

B: Mr Micawber

C: The Artful Dodger

D: Uriah Heep

62

The dingo is a wild dog from which continent?

A: Australia

B: Africa

C: South America

D: North America

63

OFFER is the acronym for the government body
set up to oversee which denationalised companies?

A: Gas

B: Water

C: Electricity

D: Telecommunications

64

Which prison featured in the TV sitcom 'Porridge'?

A: Wentworth

B: Stone Park

C: Slade

D: Wormwood Scrubs

65

Which everyday English word literally
means 'and the rest' in Latin?

A: Ditto

B: Agenda

C: Gratis

D: Etcetera

If you would like to use your 50:50 please turn to page 243
Turn to the answer section on page 257 to find out if you've won £500!

66

In which county is Stansted Airport?

◆A: Essex
◆B: Kent
◆C: Warwickshire
◆D: Oxfordshire

67

Which sea laps the east coast of Scotland?

◆A: North
◆B: Caspian
◆C: Baltic
◆D: Irish

68

What was the nickname of
Peter Jenkins in 'Grange Hill'?

◆A: Zammo
◆B: Gonch
◆C: Tucker
◆D: Ziggy

69

Which of these animals lays eggs?

◆A: Rabbit
◆B: Platypus
◆C: Dolphin
◆D: Skunk

70

What is a cauldron?

◆A: Small boat
◆B: Boiling pot
◆C: Carriage
◆D: Prayer

If you would like to use your 50:50 please turn to page 243
Turn to the answer section on page 257 to find out if you've won £500!

4 ◆ £500

71

What do we call a word formed by the letters of another in a different order?

A: Anagram

B: Adjective

C: Synonym

D: Preposition

72

Oxford is often referred to as the city of 'dreaming...' what?

A: Students

B: Dons

C: Chimneys

D: Spires

73

Which writer is best remembered for the classic vampire story 'Dracula'?

A: Mary Shelley

B: Bram Stoker

C: Charles Dickens

D: Jules Verne

74

Which of these is a type of small falcon?

A: Lancelot

B: Galahad

C: Guinevere

D: Merlin

75

Which character was played by Diana Rigg in the TV series 'The Avengers'?

A: Tara King

B: Cathy Gale

C: Purdey

D: Emma Peel

If you would like to use your 50:50 please turn to page 243
Turn to the answer section on page 257 to find out if you've won £500!

4 ◆ £500

76

Who passed sentence on Jesus?

- A: Barabbas
- B: Judas
- C: Pontius Pilate
- D: Augustus Caesar

77

Which of these primates live on the Rock of Gibraltar?

- A: Orangutans
- B: Chimpanzees
- C: Barbary apes
- D: Baboons

78

Which animals gather in groups known as prides?

- A: Wolves
- B: Lions
- C: Hippos
- D: Bears

79

If someone's hair is described as flaxen, what colour is it?

- A: Pale yellow
- B: Dark brown
- C: Ginger
- D: Jet black

80

What was the name of Olivia Newton-John's character in the film 'Grease'?

- A: Mandy
- B: Sandy
- C: Candy
- D: Randy

If you would like to use your 50:50 please turn to page 243
Turn to the answer section on page 257 to find out if you've won £500!

81

Which American state saw the first major gold rush in 1848?

A: Florida

B: Texas

C: California

D: Delaware

82

What was traditionally thrown down by a knight issuing a challenge?

A: Lance

B: Shield

C: Helmet

D: Gauntlet

83

If an MP changes party, what is he or she said to cross?

A: The Speaker

B: The floor

C: The mace

D: The House

84

The Riviera extends along the coasts of France and which other country?

A: Belgium

B: Germany

C: Spain

D: Italy

85

The Frenchman Andre Ampere gave his name to a unit of what?

A: Time

B: Electrical current

C: Weight

D: Length

If you would like to use your 50:50 please turn to page 243
Turn to the answer section on page 257 to find out if you've won £500!

86

Which river is also the name of a member of a tribe of legendary female warriors?

A: Thames

B: Nile

C: Amazon

D: Rhine

87

In which decade did the Great Train Robbery occur?

A: 1950s

B: 1960s

C: 1970s

D: 1980s

88

How many oars are used to propel a gondola?

A: One

B: Two

C: Three

D: Four

89

In a standard set of 28 dominoes, how many doubles are there?

A: Five

B: Six

C: Seven

D: Eight

90

What is the smallest breed of dog?

A: Dalmatian

B: Chihuahua

C: Golden retriever

D: Dachshund

If you would like to use your 50:50 please turn to page 243
Turn to the answer section on page 257 to find out if you've won £500!

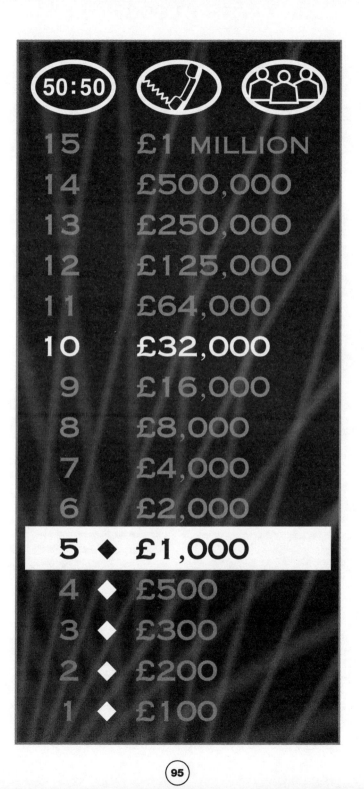

50:50	☎	👥👥

15	£1 MILLION
14	£500,000
13	£250,000
12	£125,000
11	£64,000
10	**£32,000**
9	£16,000
8	£8,000
7	£4,000
6	£2,000
5 ◆	**£1,000**
4 ◆	£500
3 ◆	£300
2 ◆	£200
1 ◆	£100

5 ◆ £1,000

1

Where was Leonardo Da Vinci born?

- A: Palermo
- B: Milan
- C: Leonardo
- D: Vinci

2

In which country was the 1992 film 'Strictly Ballroom' set?

- A: South Africa
- B: Canada
- C: New Zealand
- D: Australia

3

In which city was Joan of Arc burned at the stake in 1431?

- A: Reykjavik
- B: Rouen
- C: Rochdale
- D: Rome

4

Thomas Sopwith was famous for designing which type of vehicle?

- A: Aeroplane
- B: Hovercraft
- C: Motorcycle
- D: Train

5

In the Old Testament, who was the twin brother of Jacob?

- A: Adam
- B: Esau
- C: Methuselah
- D: Jonah

If you would like to use your 50:50 please turn to page 245
Turn to the answer section on page 257 to find out if you've won £1,000!

6

What nationality was the artist Gustav Klimt?

- A: Irish
- B: Greek
- C: Austrian
- D: Portuguese

7

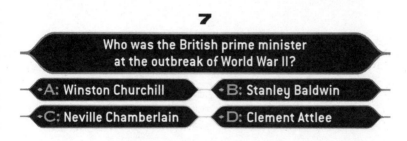

Who was the British prime minister at the outbreak of World War II?

- A: Winston Churchill
- B: Stanley Baldwin
- C: Neville Chamberlain
- D: Clement Attlee

8

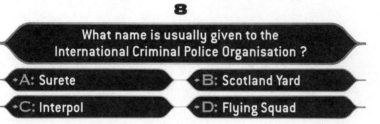

What name is usually given to the International Criminal Police Organisation ?

- A: Surete
- B: Scotland Yard
- C: Interpol
- D: Flying Squad

9

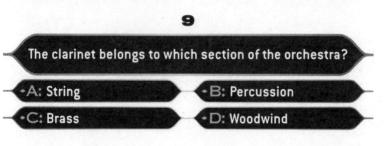

The clarinet belongs to which section of the orchestra?

- A: String
- B: Percussion
- C: Brass
- D: Woodwind

10

In which city did Sally Gunnell win an Olympic gold medal in the 400 metres hurdles?

- A: Paris
- B: Stockholm
- C: Barcelona
- D: St Louis

If you would like to use your 50:50 please turn to page 245
Turn to the answer section on page 257 to find out if you've won £1,000!

11

Which singer is famously known as 'The Man in Black'?

A: Kenny Rogers

B: Glenn Campbell

C: Johnny Cash

D: Willie Nelson

12

On a German wine bottle, what does 'Sekt' mean?

A: Fruity

B: Sour

C: Sparkling

D: Cheap

13

What name is given to a hen
which is less than one year old?

A: Henlet

B: Chickadee

C: Pullet

D: Cockerel

14

Who composed the 'Moonlight Sonata'?

A: Debussy

B: Chopin

C: Dvorak

D: Beethoven

15

Which of these parts of the body is most
important for the sense of balance?

A: Mouth

B: Nose

C: Chin

D: Ear

If you would like to use your 50:50 please turn to page 245
Turn to the answer section on page 257 to find out if you've won £1,000!

16

Of what is orange pekoe a variety?

A: Dog

B: Tea

C: Apple

D: Duck

17

What is myopia?

A: Short-sightedness

B: Deafness

C: Baldness

D: Tooth decay

18

How many animal signs are there in the Chinese calendar?

A: Three

B: Twelve

C: Seventeen

D: Forty

19

Which group had a massive hit with 'Take My Breath Away'?

A: Chicago

B: Boston

C: Berlin

D: Geneva

20

On which form of transport did Thor Heyerdahl famously cross the Pacific in 1947?

A: Rowing boat

B: Raft

C: Balloon

D: Glider

If you would like to use your 50:50 please turn to page 245
Turn to the answer section on page 257 to find out if you've won £1,000!

21

Which of these birds can fly?

- A: Penguin
- B: Puffin
- C: Ostrich
- D: Kiwi

22

Which car emblem consists of four linked circles?

- A: Subaru
- B: Toyota
- C: Citroen
- D: Audi

23

Socrates was a famous philosopher in which civilisation?

- A: Roman
- B: Greek
- C: Egyptian
- D: Chinese

24

Which single word title connects hits by Patsy Cline, Seal and Mark Morrison?

- A: Killer
- B: Crazy
- C: Girls
- D: Happy

25

What is the name of the Premium Bonds computer?

- A: Eric
- B: Ernie
- C: Reggie
- D: Arnie

If you would like to use your 50:50 please turn to page 245
Turn to the answer section on page 257 to find out if you've won £1,000!

5 ◆ £1,000

26

Which bird has species called
emperor, king and rockhopper?

A: Penguin
B: Hummingbird
C: Sparrow
D: Cuckoo

27

What nationality is the operatic tenor Placido Domingo?

A: Italian
B: Mexican
C: Argentinian
D: Spanish

28

What is the total number of spots on a standard dice?

A: Fifteen
B: Twenty
C: Twenty one
D: Twenty eight

29

Which part of a camera opens to
admit light when you take a picture?

A: Spool
B: Flash
C: Lens
D: Shutter

30

What did King Camp Gillette invent?

A: Caravan
B: Steam iron
C: Toothbrush
D: Safety razor

If you would like to use your 50:50 please turn to page 245
Turn to the answer section on page 257 to find out if you've won £1,000!

5 ◆ £1,000

31

Whose last words are said
to have been, 'Kiss me, Hardy'?

- A: Stan Laurel
- B: Horatio Nelson
- C: Mrs Hardy
- D: George V

32

Which hero was the subject of a
Disney animated feature film in 1997?

- A: Ulysses
- B: Hercules
- C: Perseus
- D: Achilles

33

Which instrument measures atmospheric pressure?

- A: Barometer
- B: Ammeter
- C: Speedometer
- D: Thermometer

34

Which bird's name means 'two under par' in golf?

- A: Duck
- B: Albatross
- C: Eagle
- D: Vulture

35

Which actor was pursued by a crop-dusting aeroplane
in the Hitchcock film 'North by Northwest'?

- A: James Stewart
- B: Cary Grant
- C: Paul Newman
- D: Gary Cooper

If you would like to use your 50:50 please turn to page 245
Turn to the answer section on page 257 to find out if you've won £1,000!

36

What is the name of the famous bobsleigh run at St Moritz?

- A: Crater Run
- B: Fun Run
- C: Death Run
- D: Cresta Run

37

In which part of the world did calypso music originate?

- A: Japan
- B: Australia
- C: West Indies
- D: South Pacific

38

Which sign of the zodiac is represented by twins?

- A: Taurus
- B: Gemini
- C: Aries
- D: Libra

39

Which TV series has a Mountie as a central character?

- A: Due South
- B: City Central
- C: Touching Evil
- D: Dawson's Creek

40

A mouflon is a wild variety of which animal?

- A: Chicken
- B: Sheep
- C: Dog
- D: Goose

If you would like to use your 50:50 please turn to page 245
Turn to the answer section on page 257 to find out if you've won £1,000!

41

Queen Anne was the daughter of which English monarch?

- A: James II
- B: Henry VIII
- C: Victoria
- D: William I

42

Who are Athos, Porthos and Aramis?

- A: Three Stooges
- B: Three Wise Men
- C: Marx Brothers
- D: Three Musketeers

43

In the 1983 horror film 'Christine', who or what was Christine?

- A: Car
- B: Lamppost
- C: Hamburger
- D: Tortoise

44

One hundred South African cents make one what?

- A: Dollar
- B: Pound
- C: Guilder
- D: Rand

45

Which of these is a Swedish pop group?

- A: The Cardigans
- B: The Sweaters
- C: The Pullovers
- D: The Jerseys

If you would like to use your 50:50 please turn to page 245
Turn to the answer section on page 257 to find out if you've won £1,000!

5 ◆ £1,000

46

Which North American animal has a
distinctive black 'mask' and a striped tail?

A: Grizzly bear

B: Bald eagle

C: Coyote

D: Raccoon

47

Which Scottish town is known as 'the home of golf'?

A: St Davids

B: St Andrews

C: St Patricks

D: St Georges

48

Which of these British birds has brilliant
greenish-blue and orange plumage?

A: Kingfisher

B: Osprey

C: Curlew

D: Swallow

49

Which word means to debase by
mixing with something inferior?

A: Adulate

B: Adjudicate

C: Advocate

D: Adulterate

50

Who won an Oscar for 'The Godfather'
but refused to accept it?

A: Marlon Brando

B: Al Pacino

C: Francis Ford Coppola

D: Diane Keaton

If you would like to use your 50:50 please turn to page 245
Turn to the answer section on page 257 to find out if you've won £1,000!

51

What is the specific collective term for a stable of racehorses?

A: Troop

B: String

C: Pack

D: Clutch

52

What are the two official languages of the Olympic Movement?

A: French and German

B: French and English

C: French and Spanish

D: French and Italian

53

What is the title of the wife of an earl?

A: Lady

B: Viscountess

C: Countess

D: Marchioness

54

Which motorcycle races are held each year on the Isle of Man?

A: BB

B: DD

C: TT

D: YY

55

What name is given to the high speed trains of Japan?

A: Rocket trains

B: Bullet trains

C: Greyhound trains

D: Eagle trains

If you would like to use your 50:50 please turn to page 245
Turn to the answer section on page 257 to find out if you've won £1,000!

5 ◆ £1,000

56

In a Punch and Judy show, what sort of animal is Toby?

- A: Crocodile
- B: Mouse
- C: Monkey
- D: Dog

57

What is the Earth's only natural satellite?

- A: Moon
- B: Pluto
- C: Krypton
- D: Sun

58

Which TV series featured the spaceship 'Liberator'?

- A: Doctor Who
- B: Blake's Seven
- C: Star Trek
- D: Gladiators

59

What is the largest member of the true deer family?

- A: Elk
- B: Roe deer
- C: Red deer
- D: Fallow deer

60

Which city hosted the 1956 Summer Olympic Games?

- A: Melbourne
- B: Manchester
- C: Milan
- D: Miami

If you would like to use your 50:50 please turn to page 245
Turn to the answer section on page 257 to find out if you've won £1,000!

5 ◆ £1,000

61

Which part of a stage projects into the audience?

- A: Pinafore
- B: Skirt
- C: Apron
- D: Petticoat

62

Who wrote the novel 'A Parliamentary Affair'?

- A: Edwina Currie
- B: Margaret Thatcher
- C: Tony Blair
- D: Robin Cook

63

Which of these soups traditionally contains fish?

- A: Minestrone
- B: Mulligatawny
- C: Chowder
- D: Cock-a-leekie

64

What is Baroness Thatcher's middle name?

- A: Harriet
- B: Hilda
- C: Hyacinth
- D: Helga

65

In a poem by Edward Lear, what did the Pobble lose while swimming the Bristol Channel?

- A: Trunks
- B: Toes
- C: Hat
- D: Fingers

If you would like to use your 50:50 please turn to page 245
Turn to the answer section on page 257 to find out if you've won £1,000!

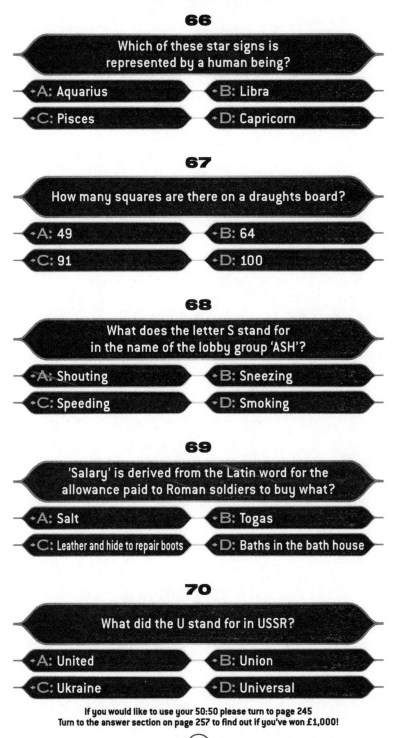

66

Which of these star signs is represented by a human being?

A: Aquarius

B: Libra

C: Pisces

D: Capricorn

67

How many squares are there on a draughts board?

A: 49

B: 64

C: 91

D: 100

68

What does the letter S stand for in the name of the lobby group 'ASH'?

A: Shouting

B: Sneezing

C: Speeding

D: Smoking

69

'Salary' is derived from the Latin word for the allowance paid to Roman soldiers to buy what?

A: Salt

B: Togas

C: Leather and hide to repair boots

D: Baths in the bath house

70

What did the U stand for in USSR?

A: United

B: Union

C: Ukraine

D: Universal

If you would like to use your 50:50 please turn to page 245
Turn to the answer section on page 257 to find out if you've won £1,000!

71

Which city used to be called New Amsterdam?

A: The Hague

B: Chicago

C: Rotterdam

D: New York

72

Which of these actors did not play Doctor Who on television?

A: Colin Baker

B: Tom Baker

C: Patrick Troughton

D: Bill Pertwee

73

The letter D is the international car registration of which country?

A: Denmark

B: Germany

C: Spain

D: Switzerland

74

Who wrote Journey to the 'Centre of the Earth'?

A: Victor Hugo

B: Jules Verne

C: Moliere

D: Gustave Flaubert

75

What was the first name of the British explorer Captain Cook?

A: Thomas

B: Mungo

C: James

D: William

If you would like to use your 50:50 please turn to page 245
Turn to the answer section on page 257 to find out if you've won £1,000!

76

Which railway station has a fictional bear named after it?

A: Waterloo
B: King's Cross
C: Paddington
D: Euston

77

Which game is played on a diamond?

A: Basketball
B: Australian rules football
C: Baseball
D: Ice hockey

78

Who was Queen Victoria's favourite ghillie?

A: John Smith
B: John Brown
C: John Jones
D: John Adams

79

In relation to cars, what does the abbreviation MOT stand for?

A: Made of Tin
B: Ministry of Transport
C: Motor Official Trader
D: Motor Operating Test

80

Which bandleader had the catchphrase 'Wakey, wakey!'?

A: Billy Cotton
B: Henry Hall
C: Glenn Miller
D: Ted Heath

If you would like to use your 50:50 please turn to page 245
Turn to the answer section on page 257 to find out if you've won £1,000!

81

Which of these words means a group of islands?

A: Archipelago
B: Fjord
C: Range
D: Canyon

82

In which month is St Valentine's Day?

A: January
B: February
C: March
D: April

83

Which composer had the middle name Amadeus?

A: Beethoven
B: Tchaikovsky
C: Mozart
D: Bach

84

What name is given to the population count that takes place every ten years in the UK?

A: Census
B: Prospectus
C: Rictus
D: Consensus

85

What was the subject of Charles Darwin's famous theory?

A: Relativity
B: Gravity
C: Evolution
D: Light

If you would like to use your 50:50 please turn to page 245
Turn to the answer section on page 257 to find out if you've won £1,000!

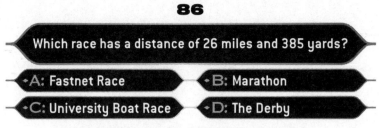

Which race has a distance of 26 miles and 385 yards?

A: Fastnet Race   B: Marathon

C: University Boat Race   D: The Derby

If you would like to use your 50:50 please turn to page 245
Turn to the answer section on page 257 to find out if you've won £1,000!

6 ◆ £2,000

1

Which of these films did not star Cher?

A: Mask
B: Mermaids
C: Misery
D: Moonstruck

2

Which of these wars began in 1950?

A: Spanish Civil War
B: Vietnam War
C: Suez War
D: Korean War

3

What was the name of the world's first test tube baby?

A: Louise Brown
B: Sarah Evans
C: Lucy Bryant
D: Sharon Fuller

4

The Franciscan order was founded by Saint Francis of where?

A: Naples
B: Verona
C: Padua
D: Assisi

5

What is the American name for the group of stars known in Britain as the Plough?

A: The Merry-go-round
B: The Big Dipper
C: The Rollercoaster
D: The Helter-skelter

If you would like to use your 50:50 please turn to page 246
Turn to the answer section on page 258 to find out if you've won £2,000!

6

In the TV series 'Blackadder Goes Forth', which character was played by Tim McInnerny?

- A: Captain Sweetheart
- B: Captain Flashheart
- C: Captain Honey
- D: Captain Darling

7

Which of these is a Welsh National Park?

- A: Lake District
- B: Brecon Beacons
- C: Peak District
- D: Exmoor

8

Which of these golf tournaments is not classed as a 'major'?

- A: US Open
- B: US Masters
- C: British Open
- D: Australian Open

9

With whom did UB40 team up for the single 'I'll Be Your Baby Tonight'?

- A: Peter Gabriel
- B: Chrissie Hynde
- C: Robert Palmer
- D: Maxi Priest

10

On which London thoroughfare is the Cenotaph?

- A: Whitehall
- B: Oxford Circus
- C: Piccadilly
- D: Kings Road

If you would like to use your 50:50 please turn to page 246
Turn to the answer section on page 258 to find out if you've won £2,000!

11

What was Dr Kildare's first name in the TV series?

A: James

B: John

C: Peter

D: Timothy

12

Which of these is a quadruped?

A: A rectangle

B: A cow

C: A person aged 40

D: A car

13

Which of these can be described as 'ovoid'?

A: Coil

B: Egg

C: Worm

D: Kidney

14

What is another term for the St Andrew's Cross?

A: Russian

B: Lorraine

C: Saltire

D: Greek

15

Who played Scarlett O'Hara in the 1939 film 'Gone with the Wind'?

A: Vivien Leigh

B: Olivia De Havilland

C: Ingrid Bergman

D: Katharine Hepburn

If you would like to use your 50:50 please turn to page 246
Turn to the answer section on page 258 to find out if you've won £2,000!

16

Which of these is a crisp salted biscuit?

A: Garibaldi
B: Ratafia
C: Florentine
D: Pretzel

17

Who composed 'Rhapsody in Blue'?

A: Cole Porter
B: Irving Berlin
C: George Gershwin
D: Aaron Copland

18

Which of these is a former name of Istanbul?

A: Constantinople
B: Rangoon
C: Sofia
D: Topkapi

19

What did the Romans call a marketplace or public square?

A: Curia
B: Basilica
C: Forum
D: Nomen

20

According to Edward Lear, the Owl and the Pussy-Cat went to sea in a boat of which colour?

A: Sky blue
B: Pea green
C: Jet black
D: Brick red

If you would like to use your 50:50 please turn to page 246
Turn to the answer section on page 258 to find out if you've won £2,000!

21

In Australia, the Melbourne Cup is the most prestigious event in which sport?

A: Rugby
B: Australian rules football
C: Horse racing
D: Cricket

22

Which group was the subject of the film 'The Great Rock 'n' Roll Swindle'?

A: The Clash
B: The Sex Pistols
C: The Doors
D: The Who

23

What is 'mal de mer'?

A: Headache
B: Seasickness
C: Homesickness
D: Vertigo

24

How many stripes appear on the flag of the USA?

A: Two
B: Three
C: Thirteen
D: Fifty

25

What was the pen name of the author Eric Blair?

A: George Eliot
B: George Bernard Shaw
C: George Orwell
D: Georges Simenon

If you would like to use your 50:50 please turn to page 246
Turn to the answer section on page 258 to find out if you've won £2,000!

26

Which lines on a map join places of equal elevation?

- A: Ley lines
- B: Contour lines
- C: Plimsoll lines
- D: Slope lines

27

On which river does the city of Vienna stand?

- A: Danube
- B: Rhone
- C: Rhine
- D: Weser

28

Which of these sports has a playing surface which is slightly raised in the middle?

- A: Snooker
- B: Crown green bowling
- C: Fencing
- D: Lawn tennis

29

Which of these is an Indian deep-fried pastry?

- A: Samosa
- B: Nan
- C: Kofta
- D: Chapatti

30

What was the title of the only Number One single for Rolf Harris?

- A: Two Little Boys
- B: Sun Arise
- C: Bluer Than Blue
- D: Stairway To Heaven

If you would like to use your 50:50 please turn to page 246
Turn to the answer section on page 258 to find out if you've won £2,000!

31

Who was Doyle's partner in 'The Professionals'?

- A: Shortie
- B: Codie
- C: Jodie
- D: Bodie

32

Located in Scotland and northern England, what are 'fells'?

- A: Lakes
- B: Woods
- C: Streams
- D: Hills

33

Which French expression denotes a set meal at a fixed price?

- A: A la carte
- B: Table d'hote
- C: Carte blanche
- D: Cordon bleu

34

When somebody suffers from mumps, which body parts swell up?

- A: Joints
- B: Ears
- C: Glands
- D: Feet

35

Which currency would you require in the Netherlands?

- A: Guilders
- B: Marks
- C: Schillings
- D: Francs

If you would like to use your 50:50 please turn to page 246
Turn to the answer section on page 258 to find out if you've won £2,000!

36

What kind of sausage would you expect to find in a hot dog?

- A: Salami
- B: Frankfurter
- C: Pepperoni
- D: Bratwurst

37

Which Shakespearean character shouts 'A horse! A horse! My kingdom for a horse!'?

- A: King Lear
- B: Richard III
- C: Macbeth
- D: Cleopatra

38

Who wrote the children's story, 'The Old Man of Lochnagar'?

- A: Prince Philip
- B: Sarah, Duchess of York
- C: Princess Margaret
- D: Prince Charles

39

Who married Prince Rainier of Monaco in 1956?

- A: Marilyn Monroe
- B: Grace Kelly
- C: Ava Gardner
- D: Judy Garland

40

Of which form of transport was a 'boneshaker' an early type?

- A: Helicopter
- B: Bicycle
- C: Car
- D: Airship

If you would like to use your 50:50 please turn to page 246
Turn to the answer section on page 258 to find out if you've won £2,000!

41

Which of these landmarks is in India?

- A: Sugar Loaf Mountain
- B: Ayers Rock
- C: Taj Mahal
- D: Pyramids of Giza

42

Which city was the first to have an underground railway?

- A: Manchester
- B: London
- C: Glasgow
- D: Newcastle

43

If a surgeon is qualified in orthopaedics, which parts of the body does he or she specialise in?

- A: Ears, nose and throat
- B: Joints, bones and muscles
- C: Heart and lungs
- D: Brain and nervous system

44

Who is Shirley MacLaine's famous film star brother?

- A: Jack Nicholson
- B: Warren Beatty
- C: Gene Hackman
- D: Paul Newman

45

Which pigment gives vegetation its green colour?

- A: Chloroform
- B: Chlorine
- C: Chlorophyll
- D: Chlorite

If you would like to use your 50:50 please turn to page 246
Turn to the answer section on page 258 to find out if you've won £2,000!

6 ◆ £2,000

46

Which station is the London terminus
for trains from Penzance?

A: Waterloo

B: Victoria

C: St. Pancras

D: Paddington

47

What name is given to the top universities in the USA?

A: Premier League

B: Laurel League

C: Super League

D: Ivy League

48

What does a claustrophobic person fear?

A: Confined spaces

B: Cats

C: Open spaces

D: Spiders

49

Which of these people lived at
Dove Cottage in the Lake District?

A: William Wordsworth

B: Charles Darwin

C: George Bernard Shaw

D: John Keats

50

What kind of Italian food is 'ciabatta'?

A: Ham

B: Cheese

C: Ice cream

D: Bread

If you would like to use your 50:50 please turn to page 246
Turn to the answer section on page 258 to find out if you've won £2,000!

51

What was Grandma Walton's first name in the TV series?

- A: Ellie
- B: Enid
- C: Edna
- D: Esther

52

Which king was killed at the Battle of Hastings?

- A: William
- B: John
- C: Edward
- D: Harold

53

Which flower is named after a beautiful youth of Greek mythology?

- A: Polyanthus
- B: Mimulus
- C: Hibiscus
- D: Narcissus

54

Which scale is used to test whether garden soil is acid, neutral or alkaline?

- A: Mercalli Scale
- B: Richter Scale
- C: pH Scale
- D: Lime Scale

55

Which of these words describes the force with which an object is impelled?

- A: Gravity
- B: Impetus
- C: Density
- D: Inertia

If you would like to use your 50:50 please turn to page 246
Turn to the answer section on page 258 to find out if you've won £2,000!

56

The beetle with jaws resembling antlers is known by what name?

A: Hind beetle

B: Elk beetle

C: Stag beetle

D: Moose beetle

57

Which fictional sailor was captain of a ship called the Black Pig?

A: Black Jake

B: Long John Silver

C: Captain Pugwash

D: Popeye

58

In which country does the Bosporus Bridge link Europe and Asia?

A: Turkey

B: Iraq

C: Greece

D: Israel

59

'Not a Penny More, Not a Penny Less' was the title of which former MP's first novel?

A: Douglas Hurd

B: Nigel West

C: Edwina Currie

D: Jeffrey Archer

60

In ancient Greece, Homer was famous in which field?

A: Mathematics

B: Philosophy

C: Poetry

D: Music

If you would like to use your 50:50 please turn to page 246
Turn to the answer section on page 258 to find out if you've won £2,000!

6 ◆ £2,000

61

Which of these animals is not a reptile?

A: Lizard
B: Crocodile
C: Toad
D: Snake

62

The alimentary canal is primarily involved with which bodily function?

A: Digestion
B: Sight
C: Reproduction
D: Smell

63

Semaphore is a method of sending signals using what?

A: Flags
B: Mirrors
C: Telegraph
D: Signal lamps

64

Which English poet was the husband of the author who wrote 'Frankenstein'?

A: Shelley
B: Byron
C: Browning
D: Blake

65

According to the Bible, with which weapon did David slay Goliath?

A: Lance
B: Arrow
C: Sling
D: Club

If you would like to use your 50:50 please turn to page 246
Turn to the answer section on page 258 to find out if you've won £2,000!

66

Which of these groups campaigned for votes for women?

A: Abolitionists

B: Luddites

C: Tolpuddle Martyrs

D: Suffragettes

67

What is used to hit the ball in a game of croquet?

A: Racquet

B: Bat

C: Foot

D: Mallet

68

Which motorway connects London and South Wales?

A: M40

B: M4

C: M5

D: M6

69

Which artistic movement was founded by Georges Braque and Pablo Picasso?

A: Triangulism

B: Cubism

C: Pentagonism

D: Octagonism

70

Which of these horse races is not one of the English 'Classics'?

A: Derby

B: Oaks

C: St Leger

D: Hennessy Gold Cup

If you would like to use your 50:50 please turn to page 246
Turn to the answer section on page 258 to find out if you've won £2,000!

71

What is the name of the peninsula occupied by Spain and Portugal?

A: Balearic Peninsula

B: Hispanic Peninsula

C: Lisboa Peninsula

D: Iberian Peninsula

72

Who was the first DJ to be heard on Radio One?

A: Jimmy Young

B: Jimmy Savile

C: Pete Murray

D: Tony Blackburn

73

Which of these is not a nickname for the Devil?

A: Old Nick

B: Old George

C: Old Harry

D: Satan

74

Which football team does TV's Alf Garnett famously support?

A: Arsenal

B: Chelsea

C: West Ham United

D: Queen's Park Rangers

If you would like to use your 50:50 please turn to page 246
Turn to the answer section on page 258 to find out if you've won £2,000!

1

What was Ray's surname in 'Dallas'?

- A: Ewing
- B: Barnes
- C: Harper
- D: Krebbs

2

What is a yashmak?

- A: Veil
- B: Bracelet
- C: Prayer mat
- D: Belt

3

What was the name of the winged horse of Greek mythology?

- A: Silver
- B: Bellerophon
- C: Champion
- D: Pegasus

4

Which actor played eight different parts in the film 'Kind Hearts and Coronets'?

- A: Laurence Olivier
- B: John Gielgud
- C: Peter Sellers
- D: Alec Guinness

5

Which year of the 20th century saw three different monarchs on the British throne?

- A: 1901
- B: 1910
- C: 1936
- D: 1952

If you would like to use your 50:50 please turn to page 247
Turn to the answer section on page 258 to find out if you've won £4,000!

6

Which of these is a Sikh place of worship?

A: Mosque

B: Cathedral

C: Synagogue

D: Gurdwara

7

Which TV character had a horse called Hercules?

A: Dick Turpin

B: Ross Poldark

C: Harold Steptoe

D: Lucy Ewing

8

Which of these is a painting by Vincent Van Gogh?

A: The Pumpkin Eaters

B: The Apple Eaters

C: The Tomato Eaters

D: The Potato Eaters

9

What was the name of the character played
by Sigourney Weaver in the 'Alien' films?

A: Dallas

B: Ripley

C: Lambert

D: Parker

10

Which king of England was executed in 1649?

A: James I

B: Charles I

C: James II

D: Charles II

If you would like to use your 50:50 please turn to page 247
Turn to the answer section on page 258 to find out if you've won £4,000!

11

What is the Celsius equivalent of 77 degrees Fahrenheit?

A: 15 degrees C

B: 20 degrees C

C: 25 degrees C

D: 30 degrees C

12

Who betrayed Jesus in the Garden of Gethsemane?

A: Judas Iscariot

B: Pontius Pilate

C: Mary Magdalene

D: Joseph of Arimathea

13

Which cartoon character does Wile E. Coyote normally chase?

A: Pepe le Pew

B: Road Runner

C: Foghorn Leghorn

D: Porky Pig

14

What is the main opera house of New York City?

A: The Metropolitan

B: The Grand

C: The Palladium

D: The Odeon

15

What nationality was the composer Mussorgsky?

A: French

B: Russian

C: Polish

D: German

If you would like to use your 50:50 please turn to page 247
Turn to the answer section on page 258 to find out if you've won £4,000!

16

Hans Holbein was the court painter to which monarch?

A: William III
B: Henry VIII
C: Elizabeth I
D: George IV

17

What is 'helix aspersa', a pest in the garden because of its liking for green vegetation?

A: Greenfly
B: Slug
C: Snail
D: Blackfly

18

Babe Ruth was famous for playing which sport?

A: Ice Hockey
B: American Football
C: Basketball
D: Baseball

19

Which of these presidents was not a Republican?

A: Gerald Ford
B: Richard Nixon
C: George Bush
D: Jimmy Carter

20

In 1993, Esha Ness 'won' which horse race that never was?

A: 1000 Guineas
B: Grand National
C: Cheltenham Gold Cup
D: Derby

If you would like to use your 50:50 please turn to page 247
Turn to the answer section on page 258 to find out if you've won £4,000!

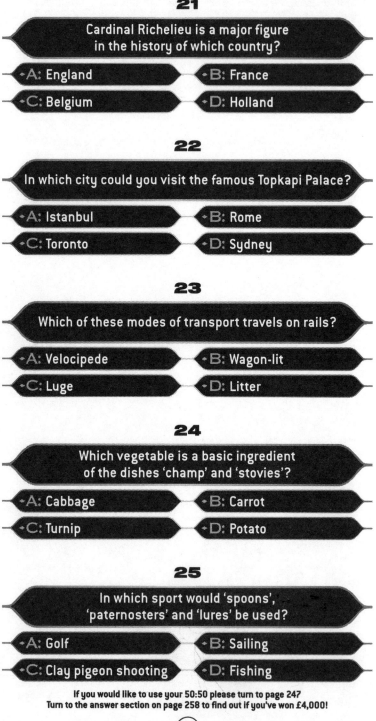

21

Cardinal Richelieu is a major figure in the history of which country?

- A: England
- B: France
- C: Belgium
- D: Holland

22

In which city could you visit the famous Topkapi Palace?

- A: Istanbul
- B: Rome
- C: Toronto
- D: Sydney

23

Which of these modes of transport travels on rails?

- A: Velocipede
- B: Wagon-lit
- C: Luge
- D: Litter

24

Which vegetable is a basic ingredient of the dishes 'champ' and 'stovies'?

- A: Cabbage
- B: Carrot
- C: Turnip
- D: Potato

25

In which sport would 'spoons', 'paternosters' and 'lures' be used?

- A: Golf
- B: Sailing
- C: Clay pigeon shooting
- D: Fishing

If you would like to use your 50:50 please turn to page 247
Turn to the answer section on page 258 to find out if you've won £4,000!

26

What name is given to a symbol on a
VDU screen of a facility available for selection?

- A: Ikon
- B: Window
- C: Cursor
- D: Port

27

Which word on champagne or sparkling
wine labels indicates that it is dry?

- A: Sec
- B: Brut
- C: Premier Cru
- D: Doux

28

Who won six World Professional Snooker
Championship titles during the 1970s?

- A: Steve Davis
- B: John Spencer
- C: Alex Higgins
- D: Ray Reardon

29

Which professionals are
called 'realtors' in North America?

- A: Undertakers
- B: Lawyers
- C: Estate agents
- D: Bankers

30

In which year was the Festival of Britain held?

- A: 1801
- B: 1851
- C: 1901
- D: 1951

If you would like to use your 50:50 please turn to page 247
Turn to the answer section on page 258 to find out if you've won £4,000!

31

Which of these vehicles is designed to travel on snow or ice?

- A: Scrambler
- B: Luge
- C: Pullman
- D: Palanquin

32

Which 'Dad's Army' actor had a Number One hit record?

- A: Arthur Lowe
- B: John Le Mesurier
- C: Ian Lavender
- D: Clive Dunn

33

Who was married to Dan Archer in the radio soap?

- A: Dolly
- B: Dolores
- C: Daphne
- D: Doris

34

Which car became known as a 'Tin Lizzie'?

- A: Austin 7
- B: Model T Ford
- C: Volkswagen Beetle
- D: Mini

35

Which country produces Mateus Rose wine?

- A: France
- B: Italy
- C: Spain
- D: Portugal

If you would like to use your 50:50 please turn to page 247
Turn to the answer section on page 258 to find out if you've won £4,000!

36

In which London park is there
a lake called the Serpentine?

- A: Green Park
- B: St James's Park
- C: Regent's Park
- D: Hyde Park

37

What was the title of the first 'Star Trek' movie?

- A: The Wrath of Khan
- B: The Voyage Home
- C: The Search for Spock
- D: The Motion Picture

38

Which character in the Sherlock Holmes
stories was an Inspector from Scotland Yard?

- A: Lestrade
- B: Hudson
- C: Mycroft
- D: Watson

39

In which body of water is the Isle of Man?

- A: North Sea
- B: Irish Sea
- C: Cardigan Bay
- D: Bristol Channel

40

According to legend, which
king tried to turn back the sea?

- A: Herod
- B: Canute
- C: John
- D: Arthur

If you would like to use your 50:50 please turn to page 247
Turn to the answer section on page 258 to find out if you've won £4,000!

41

Which of these birds is native to Africa?

A: Ostrich

B: Kiwi

C: Emu

D: Cassowary

42

'The Whale' is the alternative title of which Herman Melville novel?

A: Jaws

B: Twenty Thousand Leagues Under the Sea

C: Coral Island

D: Moby Dick

43

Which Shakespeare play begins with the words, 'If music be the food of love, play on...'?

A: Twelfth Night

B: Antony and Cleopatra

C: All's Well That Ends Well

D: Romeo and Juliet

44

What was the profession of Mrs Dale's husband in the radio soap?

A: Doctor

B: Dentist

C: Postman

D: Milkman

45

What is a dibber used for in the garden?

A: Double digging

B: Pruning trees

C: Making small holes in the ground

D: Trimming hedges

If you would like to use your 50:50 please turn to page 247
Turn to the answer section on page 258 to find out if you've won £4,000!

7 ◆ £4,000

46

Who played Batman's enemy Egghead in the TV series?

- A: Vincent Price
- B: Christopher Lee
- C: Peter Cushing
- D: Cesar Romero

47

Which professionals belong to the RIBA?

- A: Accountants
- B: Artists
- C: Archaeologists
- D: Architects

48

Which star constellation appears on the flags of Australia and New Zealand?

- A: Capricornus
- B: Southern Cross
- C: Centaurus
- D: Orion

49

Which car company introduced the Topolino model in 1936?

- A: Citroen
- B: Audi
- C: Ford
- D: Fiat

50

What is the nickname of Newcastle United Football Club?

- A: Magpies
- B: Sparrows
- C: Robins
- D: Chickens

If you would like to use your 50:50 please turn to page 247
Turn to the answer section on page 258 to find out if you've won £4,000!

51

What makes a pink gin pink?

- A: Cherry juice
- B: Elderflower essence
- C: Angostura bitters
- D: Tomato juice

52

Which actress was the mistress of King Charles II?

- A: Nell Gwyn
- B: Sarah Bernhardt
- C: Lillie Langtry
- D: Sarah Siddons

53

In which classic TV western series did Lorne Greene play Ben Cartwright?

- A: Bonanza
- B: The High Chaparral
- C: The Virginian
- D: Alias Smith and Jones

54

Which city hosted the Summer Olympic Games in 1908 and 1948?

- A: Paris
- B: Moscow
- C: Edinburgh
- D: London

55

Semprini was famous for playing which instrument?

- A: Trumpet
- B: Violin
- C: Piano
- D: Oboe

If you would like to use your 50:50 please turn to page 247
Turn to the answer section on page 258 to find out if you've won £4,000!

56

In which European country do one hundred groszy equal one zloty?

A: Germany
B: Romania
C: Austria
D: Poland

57

What is a 'magnum opus'?

A: Cannon
B: Champagne bottle
C: Great work
D: Legal document

58

What was the surname of the family of writers who lived at The Parsonage in Haworth, Yorkshire?

A: Bronte
B: Austen
C: Hardy
D: Eliot

59

The American invasion of the Bay of Pigs was an attempt to overthrow the government of which country?

A: Argentina
B: Libya
C: Cuba
D: Iraq

60

What name is given to the Japanese art of swordsmanship practised with bamboo staves?

A: Ju-jitsu
B: Aikido
C: Karate
D: Kendo

If you would like to use your 50:50 please turn to page 247
Turn to the answer section on page 258 to find out if you've won £4,000!

7 ♦ £4,000

61

What was the first name of the composer Holst?

A: Gustav
B: Frederick
C: Charles
D: Eric

62

Which musical features the song 'I Could Have Danced All Night'?

A: The King and I
B: My Fair Lady
C: The Sound of Music
D: Oklahoma!

63

What is a firkin?

A: Winter garment
B: Fruit
C: Ornament
D: Barrel

64

Who won the 1997 US Masters golf tournament?

A: Lee Westwood
B: Colin Montgomerie
C: Tiger Woods
D: Mark O'Meara

65

From which animal is 'morocco' leather obtained?

A: Goat
B: Camel
C: Sheep
D: Ostrich

If you would like to use your 50:50 please turn to page 247
Turn to the answer section on page 258 to find out if you've won £4,000!

66

Who played Thelma in the film 'Thelma and Louise'?

A: Geena Davis
B: Annette Bening
C: Juliette Lewis
D: Sally Field

67

Indian clarified butter used for frying and baking is known as what?

A: Ghee
B: Samosa
C: Korma
D: Biriani

68

Which of the following was one of Robin Hood's merry men?

A: Will Scarlett
B: Will Greene
C: Will Browne
D: Will Whyte

69

Which TV doctor was played by Sylvester McCoy?

A: Dr Kildare
B: Dr Finlay
C: Dr Who
D: Dr McCoy

70

In Greek mythology, which king could turn everything he touched into gold?

A: Canute
B: Midas
C: Arthur
D: Ulysses

If you would like to use your 50:50 please turn to page 247
Turn to the answer section on page 258 to find out if you've won £4,000!

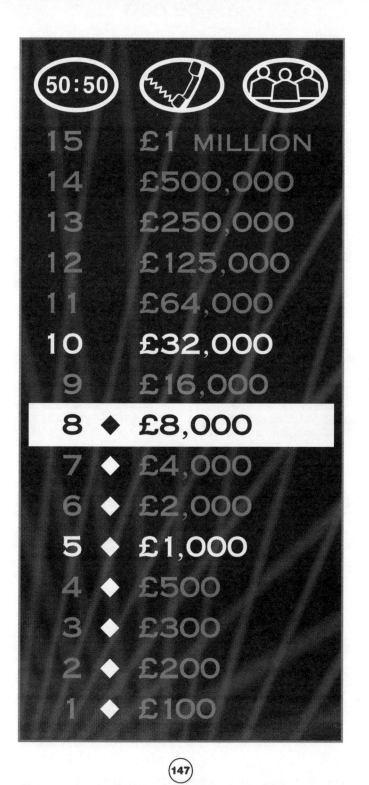

8 ◆ £8,000

1

What is the name of the TV news company in 'Drop The Dead Donkey'?

- A: Globelink News
- B: Transworld News
- C: United Broadcasting
- D: KYTV

2

In which city is the Hermitage Museum?

- A: Paris
- B: Helsinki
- C: Copenhagen
- D: Saint Petersburg

3

Where is Michelangelo's painting 'The Creation of Adam'?

- A: St. Mark's Cathedral
- B: Sistine Chapel
- C: National Gallery
- D: Louvre

4

In which country did the Impressionist art movement begin?

- A: Great Britain
- B: Italy
- C: France
- D: The Netherlands

5

Who assassinated Senator Robert Kennedy in 1968?

- A: Sirhan Sirhan
- B: Lee Harvey Oswald
- C: James Earl Ray
- D: John Wilkes Booth

If you would like to use your 50:50 please turn to page 248
Turn to the answer section on page 259 to find out if you've won £8,000!

6

Who discovered X-rays?

A: Thomas Edison
B: John Logie Baird
C: Marie Curie
D: Wilhelm Roentgen

7

What is the chemical symbol for lead?

A: K
B: Hg
C: L
D: Pb

8

C is the chemical symbol for which element?

A: Copper
B: Calcium
C: Carbon
D: Chlorine

9

What is the cube of the number eight?

A: 512
B: 64
C: 216
D: 16

10

Clarice Cliff is best known for designing what?

A: Jewellery
B: Furniture
C: Dolls
D: Pottery

If you would like to use your 50:50 please turn to page 248
Turn to the answer section on page 259 to find out if you've won £8,000!

11

Which of these cars was designed by Alec Issigonis?

A: Citroen 2CV

B: Rolls Royce Silver Ghost

C: Volkswagen Beetle

D: Morris Minor

12

Which song is set to music from one of Elgar's 'Pomp and Circumstance' marches?

A: Jerusalem

B: Rule, Britannia

C: Land of Hope and Glory

D: Auld Lang Syne

13

Of which country was Nicolae Ceausescu the president?

A: Bulgaria

B: Romania

C: Hungary

D: East Germany

14

Which politician gave up the title of Viscount Stansgate?

A: Alec Douglas-Home

B: Tony Benn

C: Michael Foot

D: Edward Heath

15

Used in dentistry, an amalgam is an alloy of which metal with other metals?

A: Gold

B: Mercury

C: Iron

D: Copper

If you would like to use your 50:50 please turn to page 248
Turn to the answer section on page 259 to find out if you've won £8,000!

16

What nationality is the ballerina Alicia Markova?

A: French
B: Russian
C: American
D: British

17

Who had a UK hit single in 1992 with 'Save the Best for Last'?

A: Deniece Williams
B: Andy Williams
C: Vanessa Williams
D: John Williams

18

In American football, how many points are awarded for a field goal?

A: Two
B: Three
C: Four
D: Five

19

Which Italian model had a number three hit in 1988 with 'Boys (Summertime Love)'?

A: Spagna
B: Sabrina
C: Selina
D: Semolina

20

What is the SI unit of illumination?

A: Lux
B: Candela
C: Watt
D: Kelvin

If you would like to use your 50:50 please turn to page 248
Turn to the answer section on page 259 to find out if you've won £8,000!

21

Which instrument records the speed of and distance covered by a vehicle?

- A: Tachograph
- B: Pantograph
- C: Hygrograph
- D: Chronograph

22

Which golfing expression means 'to be ahead by as many holes as there are holes left to play'?

- A: Bogey
- B: Dormy
- C: Par
- D: Birdie

23

Which girl's name was the title of a top ten single for Kool and the Gang in 1984?

- A: Michelle
- B: Maria
- C: Linda
- D: Joanna

24

Which of these island groups is situated in the Indian Ocean?

- A: Canary Islands
- B: Hawaii
- C: Bahamas
- D: Maldives

25

'Diwali', or the Festival of Lights, is celebrated in which religion?

- A: Hinduism
- B: Islam
- C: Buddhism
- D: Judaism

If you would like to use your 50:50 please turn to page 248
Turn to the answer section on page 259 to find out if you've won £8,000!

26

'Au' is the chemical symbol for which metal?

A: Gold

B: Silver

C: Lead

D: Mercury

27

What nationality is former World Motor Racing Champion Keke Rosberg?

A: Belgian

B: Swedish

C: Danish

D: Finnish

28

What is the most famous tourist attraction in Lake Havasu City, Arizona?

A: London Bridge

B: The Grand Canyon

C: Niagara Falls

D: Abraham Lincoln's birthplace

29

What sort of letter is an 'encyclical'?

A: Begging letter

B: Chain letter

C: Love letter

D: Papal letter

30

In which country is Fez, home of the famous hat?

A: Turkey

B: Morocco

C: Algeria

D: Tunisia

If you would like to use your 50:50 please turn to page 248
Turn to the answer section on page 259 to find out if you've won £8,000!

31

Which pop group had a 1970s hit with 'Shang-a-Lang'?

- A: Mud
- B: Bay City Rollers
- C: Wizzard
- D: Showaddywaddy

32

Which of these is an example of an acronym?

- A: Sizzle
- B: Bitter-sweet
- C: Wellington
- D: NIMBY

33

As what is Henry Cecil famous?

- A: Racehorse trainer
- B: Fashion designer
- C: Wine expert
- D: Photographer

34

Which US state is nicknamed the Empire State?

- A: New York
- B: California
- C: Alaska
- D: Texas

35

During an astrological year, which sign of the zodiac comes after Taurus but before Cancer?

- A: Gemini
- B: Libra
- C: Virgo
- D: Aries

If you would like to use your 50:50 please turn to page 248
Turn to the answer section on page 259 to find out if you've won £8,000!

36

'Suffolk Punch' and 'Hackney' are types of what?

- A: Carriage
- B: Wrestling style
- C: Cocktail
- D: Horse

37

How many people found refuge in Noah's Ark?

- A: One
- B: Two
- C: Four
- D: Eight

38

Brass is usually an alloy of copper and which other metal?

- A: Gold
- B: Zinc
- C: Silver
- D: Platinum

39

Which name described a medieval knight who travelled around in search of adventures?

- A: Knight Templar
- B: Knight Hospitaller
- C: Knight Errant
- D: Knight Bachelor

40

What does the Australian word 'dinkum' mean?

- A: Small
- B: Outside
- C: English
- D: Honest

If you would like to use your 50:50 please turn to page 248
Turn to the answer section on page 259 to find out if you've won £8,000!

41

What is the British way of spelling the word that refers to the document you need for driving a car?

- A: Licence
- B: Lisense
- C: License
- D: Lisence

42

Which area of France, the River Rhone delta, is famous for its white horses, bulls and nature reserve?

- A: Camargue
- B: Dordogne
- C: Languedoc
- D: Aquitaine

43

What is the common name for the flower sometimes called an 'antirrhinum'?

- A: Wallflower
- B: Delphinium
- C: Snapdragon
- D: Foxglove

44

What is the name of the college in Britain where officers train for the RAF?

- A: Cosford
- B: Culdrose
- C: Cranwell
- D: Kemble

45

What type of equipment was made and repaired by a 'wainwright'?

- A: Nails
- B: Wagons
- C: Saddles
- D: Ploughs

If you would like to use your 50:50 please turn to page 248
Turn to the answer section on page 259 to find out if you've won £8,000!

46

Which trained professional uses a theodolyte in the course of his or her work?

- A: Sea captain
- B: Surgeon
- C: Graphic designer
- D: Surveyor

47

Which former racing driver set up his own international airline?

- A: Alain Prost
- B: Jackie Stewart
- C: Niki Lauda
- D: Nigel Mansell

48

What was the first Beatles record to hit the top of the UK singles charts?

- A: Lady Madonna
- B: Hey Jude
- C: From Me To You
- D: Yellow Submarine

49

Battledore was an early form of which sport?

- A: Fencing
- B: Badminton
- C: Croquet
- D: Judo

50

What is the name of Watford Football Club's home ground?

- A: Parsonage Road
- B: Vicarage Road
- C: Abbey Road
- D: Priory Road

If you would like to use your 50:50 please turn to page 248
Turn to the answer section on page 259 to find out if you've won £8,000!

51

Which of these characters features in Oscar Wilde's play 'The Importance of Being Earnest'?

A: Madame Arcati
B: Lady Teazle
C: Mrs Malaprop
D: Lady Bracknell

52

Which music hall entertainer was known as 'The Prime Minister of Mirth'?

A: Robb Wilton
B: Max Miller
C: Tommy Trinder
D: George Robey

53

First heard in 1948, which radio series featured Jim, Mary and their family?

A: Waggoners' Walk
B: Life with the Lyons
C: Take It From Here
D: Mrs Dale's Diary

54

Which Shakespeare play features the characters Shylock and Portia?

A: The Merchant of Venice
B: Twelfth Night
C: Titus Andronicus
D: The Winter's Tale

55

Which TV medical drama series was set in Oxbridge General Hospital?

A: Dr Kildare
B: Angels
C: Emergency Ward Ten
D: General Hospital

If you would like to use your 50:50 please turn to page 248
Turn to the answer section on page 259 to find out if you've won £8,000!

8 ♦ £8,000

56

Who was the first host of the
TV game show 'The Golden Shot'?

A: Norman Vaughan
B: Jackie Rae
C: Bob Monkhouse
D: Charlie Williams

57

Which pop group took its name from a
character in the science fiction film 'Barbarella'?

A: Depeche Mode
B: Def Leppard
C: Duran Duran
D: Deep Purple

58

Which order of monks is noted
for taking vows of silence?

A: Trappist
B: Franciscan
C: Dominican
D: Capuchin

59

What was the nickname of King Charles II?

A: The Mad Monarch
B: The Miserable Monarch
C: The Merry Monarch
D: The Morose Monarch

60

What was the nickname of the
German statesman Otto von Bismarck?

A: The Iron Duke
B: The Iron General
C: The Iron Soldier
D: The Iron Chancellor

If you would like to use your 50:50 please turn to page 248
Turn to the answer section on page 259 to find out if you've won £8,000!

61

The liqueur cassis is made from which fruit?

A: Cherry
B: Orange
C: Strawberry
D: Blackcurrant

62

A mercer would have traded mainly in which type of goods?

A: Glass
B: Textiles
C: Silver
D: Food

63

From which plant is the heart-drug digitalis obtained?

A: Foxglove
B: Bluebell
C: Rose
D: Marigold

64

'The Scream' is a famous work by which artist?

A: Edvard Munch
B: Salvador Dali
C: Pablo Picasso
D: Edgar Degas

65

The Nilsson song 'Everybody's Talkin' became a hit when it featured in which film?

A: Midnight Cowboy
B: The Graduate
C: Love Story
D: Shampoo

If you would like to use your 50:50 please turn to page 248
Turn to the answer section on page 259 to find out if you've won £8,000!

66

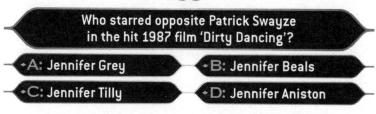

Who starred opposite Patrick Swayze
in the hit 1987 film 'Dirty Dancing'?

A: Jennifer Grey

B: Jennifer Beals

C: Jennifer Tilly

D: Jennifer Aniston

If you would like to use your 50:50 please turn to page 248
Turn to the answer section on page 259 to find out if you've won £8,000!

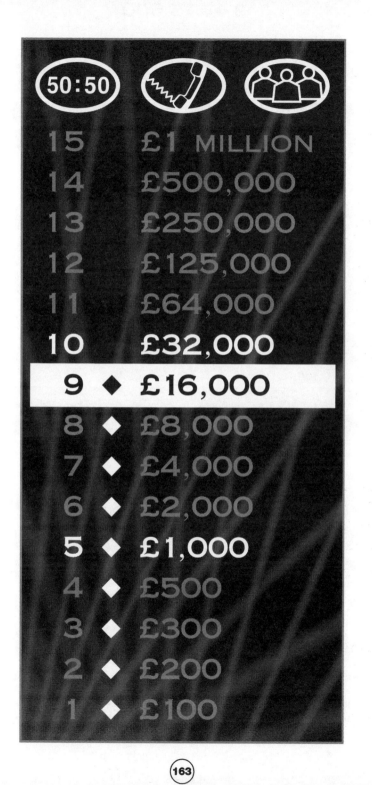

1

Which artist died in Polynesia in 1903?

- A: Gauguin
- B: Monet
- C: Degas
- D: Chagall

2

Who played Nicole Kidman's husband in the 1995 movie 'To Die For'?

- A: Matt Dillon
- B: Tom Cruise
- C: Rob Lowe
- D: Brad Pitt

3

What was the nickname of King George III?

- A: Farmer George
- B: Gentleman George
- C: Jolly George
- D: Sailor George

4

Which saint was the first Archbishop of Canterbury?

- A: Peter
- B: Alban
- C: Augustine
- D: George

5

Which specific term describes a plant, especially a lettuce, that suddenly and prematurely goes to seed?

- A: Bolting
- B: Welshing
- C: Scuttling
- D: Pelting

If you would like to use your 50:50 please turn to page 249
Turn to the answer section on page 259 to find out if you've won £16,000!

6

Which artistic movement was founded
by Hunt, Millais and Rossetti?

- A: Surrealists
- B: Arts and Crafts
- C: Fauvists
- D: Pre-Raphaelites

7

Which of these world leaders died in 1953?

- A: Winston Churchill
- B: Josef Stalin
- C: Franklin D. Roosevelt
- D: Konrad Adenauer

8

Which painting by Manet caused a scandal in 1863?

- A: Dinner on the Terrace
- B: Luncheon on the Grass
- C: Supper by the River
- D: Breakfast in Bed

9

Henrietta Maria was the wife of which English king?

- A: Charles I
- B: Charles II
- C: Henry V
- D: Edward V

10

In which country is the opera 'Aida' set?

- A: India
- B: Egypt
- C: China
- D: Thailand

If you would like to use your 50:50 please turn to page 249
Turn to the answer section on page 259 to find out if you've won £16,000!

11

Which character was played by
Ewan McGregor in the 1996 film 'Emma'?

A: Mr Knightley
B: Frank Churchill
C: Mr Elton
D: Robert Martin

12

What was the name of the suffragette killed when
she fell under the king's horse at the 1913 Derby?

A: Mary Richardson
B: Nancy Astor
C: Emily Davison
D: Emmeline Pankhurst

13

What does a deltiologist collect?

A: Postcards
B: Stamps
C: Ties
D: Parking tickets

14

How many British monarchs
belonged to the House of Hanover?

A: Two
B: Four
C: Six
D: Eight

15

Who directed the 1992 film 'The Crying Game'?

A: Alan Parker
B: Neil Jordan
C: Mike Figgis
D: Stephen Frears

If you would like to use your 50:50 please turn to page 249
Turn to the answer section on page 259 to find out if you've won £16,000!

16

In which religion is the Aga Khan a leader?

A: Buddhism
B: Islam
C: Hinduism
D: Christianity

17

In which city was Wolfgang Amadeus Mozart born?

A: Salzburg
B: Vienna
C: Berlin
D: Prague

18

Who was the third president of the United States?

A: Thomas Jefferson
B: John Adams
C: Abraham Lincoln
D: James Madison

19

Whose third law of motion states that every action has an equal and opposite reaction?

A: Newton's
B: Boyle's
C: Einstein's
D: Avogadro's

20

In knitting, what is the name of the stitch made by doing a plain stitch backwards?

A: Purl
B: Curl
C: Whurl
D: Gurl

If you would like to use your 50:50 please turn to page 249
Turn to the answer section on page 259 to find out if you've won £16,000!

21

Who is the Earl of Chester?

A: Prince Andrew
B: Prince Philip
C: Prince William
D: Prince Charles

22

John, Johannesburg and Jupiter are all names, but what type of word is a 'name'?

A: Proper noun
B: Pronoun
C: Preposition
D: Adjective

23

In which city was the Prophet Muhammad born?

A: Jerusalem
B: Medina
C: Mecca
D: Damascus

24

Where did Richard Wagner found an opera festival in 1876?

A: Bonn
B: Bayreuth
C: Brussels
D: Birmingham

25

What type of transport is a barouche?

A: Carriage
B: Boat
C: Sledge
D: Bicycle

If you would like to use your 50:50 please turn to page 249
Turn to the answer section on page 259 to find out if you've won £16,000!

9 ♦ £16,000

26

Which of the Gospel writers
is the patron saint of Venice?

- A: Matthew
- B: Mark
- C: Luke
- D: John

27

Who composed the music for the ballet 'Swan Lake'?

- A: Chopin
- B: Tchaikovsky
- C: Liszt
- D: Stravinsky

28

What is the process in which plants
use light-energy to form sugars?

- A: Osmosis
- B: Phyllotaxis
- C: Photosynthesis
- D: Thermotropism

29

Which of these prime ministers was a Conservative?

- A: Henry Campbell-Bannerman
- B: Benjamin Disraeli
- C: William Gladstone
- D: Ramsay MacDonald

30

Where did Manchester United play
their home matches between 1941 and 1949?

- A: Old Trafford Cricket Ground
- B: Wembley
- C: Salford Rugby League Ground
- D: Maine Road

If you would like to use your 50:50 please turn to page 249
Turn to the answer section on page 259 to find out if you've won £16,000!

9 ◆ £16,000

31

To what did Prince Louis of Battenberg change his family name in 1917?

- A: Windsor
- B: Hanover
- C: Bergman
- D: Mountbatten

32

What was Tony Nelson's job in the 1960s sitcom 'I Dream of Jeannie'?

- A: Airline pilot
- B: Fireman
- C: Astronaut
- D: Doctor

33

With which football club did George Best end his career?

- A: Bournemouth
- B: Fulham
- C: Los Angeles Aztecs
- D: New York Cosmos

34

Which racecourse was founded by Queen Anne in 1711?

- A: Newmarket
- B: Epsom
- C: Aintree
- D: Ascot

35

What is the subtitle of the film 'A Nightmare on Elm Street: Part Four'?

- A: Dream Warriors
- B: Freddy's Revenge
- C: The Dream Master
- D: The Dream Child

If you would like to use your 50:50 please turn to page 249
Turn to the answer section on page 259 to find out if you've won £16,000!

36

Who wrote the opera 'Turandot'?

A: Verdi
B: Rossini
C: Bellini
D: Puccini

37

In boxing, which of these categories
is closest in weight to flyweight?

A: Featherweight
B: Bantamweight
C: Lightweight
D: Welterweight

38

Who played Detective Sergeant
John Watt in the TV series 'Z Cars'?

A: Brian Blessed
B: Frank Windsor
C: Stratford Johns
D: Joss Ackland

39

Where are the present headquarters of Interpol?

A: Austria
B: Switzerland
C: Belgium
D: France

40

What does the letter M stand for
in the military abbreviation REME?

A: Mission
B: Mechanical
C: Medical
D: Marine

If you would like to use your 50:50 please turn to page 249
Turn to the answer section on page 259 to find out if you've won £16,000!

41

In Egyptian mythology, which of these became ruler of the underworld?

- A: Osiris
- B: Ra
- C: Isis
- D: Horus

42

Who was the original presenter of TV's 'Call My Bluff'?

- A: Robert Robinson
- B: Bob Holness
- C: Robert Morley
- D: Robin Ray

43

Who was Britain's first World Heavyweight Boxing Champion of the 20th century?

- A: Frank Bruno
- B: Henry Cooper
- C: Herbie Hide
- D: Lennox Lewis

44

In which industry was Lord Nuffield a pioneer?

- A: Steel
- B: Car manufacturing
- C: Newspapers
- D: Oil

45

In the USA, what is the equivalent of the Bank of England?

- A: Fort Knox
- B: Federal Reserve
- C: Bank of America
- D: First National Bank

If you would like to use your 50:50 please turn to page 249
Turn to the answer section on page 259 to find out if you've won £16,000!

46

What number is represented by 'MCM' in Roman numerals?

A: 900

B: 1400

C: 1900

D: 2900

47

Who became Queen of the Netherlands in 1980?

A: Anna

B: Wilhelmina

C: Beatrix

D: Victoria

48

Who has a secretary called Miss Lemon?

A: Perry Mason

B: Hercule Poirot

C: Columbo

D: Lord Peter Wimsey

49

What is the name for a short pithy saying such as 'In for a penny, in for a pound'?

A: Simile

B: Epithet

C: Proverb

D: Analogy

50

Mountains and desert make up two thirds of the three and a half million square miles of which country?

A: Japan

B: Bangladesh

C: Nepal

D: China

If you would like to use your 50:50 please turn to page 249
Turn to the answer section on page 259 to find out if you've won £16,000!

51

Which types of flowers are described as 'ericaceous'?

A: Daisies

B: Heathers

C: Roses

D: Pansies

52

Which monarch succeeded King George IV?

A: George V

B: William IV

C: Victoria

D: Anne

53

Which Shakespeare play features the line:
'Neither a borrower, nor a lender be'?

A: Hamlet

B: Macbeth

C: Othello

D: The Merchant of Venice

54

Which former 'Blue Peter' presenter
once played a 'Doctor Who' assistant?

A: Peter Purves

B: Valerie Singleton

C: John Noakes

D: Sarah Greene

55

Which Gilbert and Sullivan operetta has the
alternative title 'The Lass That Loved A Sailor'?

A: Ruddigore

B: The Pirates of Penzance

C: HMS Pinafore

D: The Gondoliers

If you would like to use your 50:50 please turn to page 249
Turn to the answer section on page 259 to find out if you've won £16,000!

9 ◆ £16,000

56

St Matthew is the patron saint
of which of these professions?

A: Doctors

B: Dentists

C: Estate agents

D: Tax collectors

57

What name is given to the
Japanese art of flower arrangement?

A: Batik

B: Origami

C: Bonsai

D: Ikebana

58

What is the name of the main
international airport in Venice?

A: Giuseppe Verdi

B: Marco Polo

C: Leonardo da Vinci

D: Michelangelo

59

What was a dandy-horse?

A: Donkey

B: Bicycle

C: Cart

D: Tram

60

Which shellfish are used to
make the dish 'coquilles St Jacques'?

A: Cockles

B: Scallops

C: Mussels

D: Whelks

If you would like to use your 50:50 please turn to page 249
Turn to the answer section on page 259 to find out if you've won £16,000!

61

Which type of porcelain is
made near Dresden in Germany ?

◆A: Delft
◆B: Spode

◆C: Meissen
◆D: Wedgwood

62

What would a military officer mean by a Sam Browne?

◆A: Shoulder belt
◆B: Kit bag

◆C: Bath
◆D: Fitness run

If you would like to use your 50:50 please turn to page 249
Turn to the answer section on page 259 to find out if you've won £16,000!

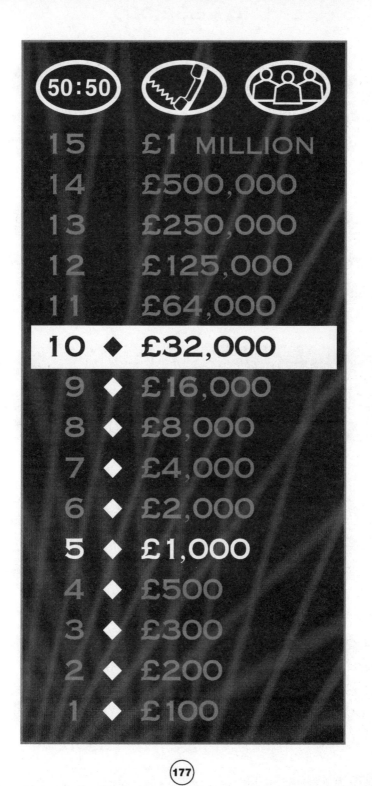

1

Which TV creatures ate Blue String Pudding?

A: The Flumps

B: The Clangers

C: The Wombles

D: The Smurfs

2

Who painted the ceiling of the Banqueting House of Whitehall Palace?

A: Rubens

B: Rembrandt

C: Renoir

D: Raphael

3

By what name is acetylsalicylic acid more commonly known?

A: Vitamin C

B: Aspirin

C: Vinegar

D: Baking powder

4

Who invented the spinning jenny?

A: Richard Arkwright

B: James Hargreaves

C: James Watt

D: Samuel Crompton

5

Before becoming vice president of the USA, Al Gore was a senator for which state?

A: Alabama

B: Mississippi

C: Florida

D: Tennessee

If you would like to use your 50:50 please turn to page 250
Turn to the answer section on page 260 to find out if you've won £32,000!

6

Which religious movement was
founded by Mary Baker Eddy?

A: Jehovah's Witnesses
B: Christian Science
C: Salvation Army
D: 7th-Day Adventists

7

Which of these is an opera by Giuseppe Verdi?

A: King Lear
B: Hamlet
C: Julius Caesar
D: Othello

8

Which explorer became an MP in 1895?

A: Henry Morton Stanley
B: David Livingstone
C: James Cook
D: Robert Falcon Scott

9

Niagara Falls, on the border between the
USA and Canada, are situated on which river?

A: Niagara
B: Erie
C: Ontario
D: St Lawrence

10

In the film 'Bad Day at Black Rock',
Spencer Tracy's character has only one what?

A: Leg
B: Eye
C: Ear
D: Arm

If you would like to use your 50:50 please turn to page 250
Turn to the answer section on page 260 to find out if you've won £32,000!

11

Which of these is not a recognised
ruling body in professional boxing?

A: WBO
B: WBC
C: WBF
D: WBA

12

Which of these Beatles songs
was released on the Apple label?

A: Love Me Do
B: Paperback Writer
C: Let It Be
D: Lady Madonna

13

In which George Eliot novel does
the character Tertius Lydgate appear?

A: The Mill On The Floss
B: Adam Bede
C: Middlemarch
D: Silas Marner

14

Which of these people was alive in the year 100 BC?

A: Hannibal
B: Julius Caesar
C: Confucius
D: Cleopatra

15

How many tricks must a bridge player
take to make a contract of four spades?

A: Four
B: Seven
C: Ten
D: Thirteen

If you would like to use your 50:50 please turn to page 250
Turn to the answer section on page 260 to find out if you've won £32,000!

16

'Zucchero' is the Italian word for which food?

A: Courgettes
B: Broccoli
C: Flour
D: Sugar

17

Who is the most senior member of the Queen's Household?

A: Lord Chamberlain
B: Lord Privy Seal
C: Lord Chancellor
D: Black Rod

18

Which of these shoes are made of wood?

A: Espadrille
B: Chukka
C: Chappal
D: Patten

19

Where would you find 'fiddles' on board a boat?

A: At the top of the mast
B: In the binnacle
C: Around the edges of tabletops
D: Attached to the anchor

20

Which is the largest city in the USA's largest state?

A: Dallas
B: Los Angeles
C: New York
D: Anchorage

If you would like to use your 50:50 please turn to page 250
Turn to the answer section on page 260 to find out if you've won £32,000!

21

What does the archer fish shoot at its prey?

A: Water
B: Venom
C: Small stones
D: Blood

22

Which of these spices comes from tree bark?

A: Turmeric
B: Cinnamon
C: Nutmeg
D: Ginger

23

By what name is Camille Javal better known?

A: Brigitte Bardot
B: Greta Garbo
C: Marlene Dietrich
D: Jeanne Moreau

24

'Per Ardua Ad Astra' is the motto of which organisation?

A: NASA
B: The Salvation Army
C: The BBC
D: The RAF

25

Who wrote 'Das Kapital'?

A: Lenin
B: Stalin
C: Trotsky
D: Marx

If you would like to use your 50:50 please turn to page 250
Turn to the answer section on page 260 to find out if you've won £32,000!

26

Where did Moses receive the Ten Commandments?

- A: Mount Ararat
- B: Mount of Olives
- C: Mount Sinai
- D: Mount Olympus

27

Which James Bond actor starred in the Disney film 'The Rocketeer'?

- A: Pierce Brosnan
- B: Sean Connery
- C: Timothy Dalton
- D: Roger Moore

28

Which vowel in Morse code is represented by a single dot?

- A: A
- B: E
- C: I
- D: O

29

What is a positive electrode called?

- A: Anode
- B: Cathode
- C: Diode
- D: Triode

30

What was James Herbert's first novel?

- A: The Survivor
- B: Fluke
- C: The Fog
- D: The Rats

If you would like to use your 50:50 please turn to page 250
Turn to the answer section on page 260 to find out if you've won £32,000!

31

What is the inscription on the George Cross?

- A: For Valour
- B: For Bravery
- C: For Heroism
- D: For Gallantry

32

Which word follows 'fire' to give a gas found in mines?

- A: Dust
- B: Dog
- C: Damp
- D: Dragon

33

What does 'impecunious' mean?

- A: Poor
- B: Cheeky
- C: Bald
- D: Ugly

34

Which of these Oasis songs did not reach number one in the UK singles chart?

- A: Wonderwall
- B: Some Might Say
- C: D'You Know What I Mean
- D: All Around The World

35

Which of these units of measurement is the largest?

- A: Gill
- B: Gallon
- C: Bushel
- D: Peck

If you would like to use your 50:50 please turn to page 250
Turn to the answer section on page 260 to find out if you've won £32,000!

36

What instrument does a 'timpanist' play?

A: Snare drum

B: Steel drum

C: Bass drum

D: Kettle drum

37

Which of the following conditions is a form of bursitis?

A: Mumps

B: Housemaid's knee

C: Hiccups

D: Hay fever

38

For most of its length, the International Date Line is how many degrees away from the Prime Meridian?

A: 90 degrees

B: 100 degrees

C: 180 degrees

D: 360 degrees

39

Who led a slaves' revolt against Rome in 73 BC?

A: Spartacus

B: Mark Antony

C: Brutus

D: Ben Hur

40

What is traditionally given as a 30th wedding anniversary gift?

A: Crystal

B: Coral

C: Pearl

D: Ruby

If you would like to use your 50:50 please turn to page 250
Turn to the answer section on page 260 to find out if you've won £32,000!

41

Which painter had the surname Van Rijn?

- A: Michelangelo
- B: Rembrandt
- C: Magritte
- D: Titian

42

Which of these religions was founded first?

- A: Buddhism
- B: Christianity
- C: Islam
- D: Sikhism

43

What did a chandler originally make?

- A: Rope
- B: Linen
- C: Candles
- D: Shoes

44

What is the literal meaning of the word 'gymnasium'?

- A: Exercise hall
- B: Physical fitness
- C: Exercise naked
- D: Keeping fit

45

What is the name for a word like 'radar' or 'scuba', made up from initials?

- A: Antonym
- B: Anagram
- C: Acrostic
- D: Acronym

If you would like to use your 50:50 please turn to page 250
Turn to the answer section on page 260 to find out if you've won £32,000!

46

What was the title of the novel that won
the Booker Prize for Salman Rushdie in 1981?

- A: Midnight's Children
- B: The Satanic Verses
- C: The Moor's Last Sigh
- D: Haroun and the Sea of Stories

47

In which county are England's
highest mountain and largest lake?

- A: Yorkshire
- B: Lancashire
- C: Derbyshire
- D: Cumbria

48

In the 1983 film 'The Big Chill', who played
the corpse in the opening credit sequence?

- A: Kevin Costner
- B: Mel Gibson
- C: Tom Hanks
- D: Richard Gere

49

A plant with the Latin name 'brassica'
belongs to which vegetable family?

- A: Cabbage
- B: Marrow
- C: Carrot
- D: Pea

50

Saint Cecilia is the patron saint of what or whom?

- A: Music
- B: Nurses
- C: Bakers
- D: Lost causes

If you would like to use your 50:50 please turn to page 250
Turn to the answer section on page 260 to find out if you've won £32,000!

51

What was the name of the ship of
Jacques Cousteau, the underwater explorer?

A: Echo
B: Calypso
C: Ariadne
D: Daphne

52

Which state has the most seats in
the American House of Representatives?

A: New York
B: California
C: Texas
D: Pennsylvania

53

Which Noel Coward play formed the basis
for the classic film 'Brief Encounter'?

A: Blithe Spirit
B: The Vortex
C: Still Life
D: Private Lives

54

Which singer was known as 'The Swedish Nightingale'?

A: Adelina Patti
B: Maria Callas
C: Jenny Lind
D: Nellie Melba

55

The 1960s TV series 'Pardon the Expression' featured
which former 'Coronation Street' character ?

A: Leonard Swindley
B: Dennis Tanner
C: Minnie Caldwell
D: David Barlow

If you would like to use your 50:50 please turn to page 250
Turn to the answer section on page 260 to find out if you've won £32,000!

56

Which coat, without shoulder seams,
has sleeves to the collar?

A: Reefer

B: Ulster

C: Duffle

D: Raglan

57

Which Pacific island group was called
the Sandwich Islands by Captain Cook?

A: Tonga

B: The Solomons

C: Hawaii

D: Fiji

58

Who was known as 'America's Sweetheart'?

A: Vera Lynn

B: Hedy Lamarr

C: Clara Bow

D: Mary Pickford

If you would like to use your 50:50 please turn to page 250
Turn to the answer section on page 260 to find out if you've won £32,000!

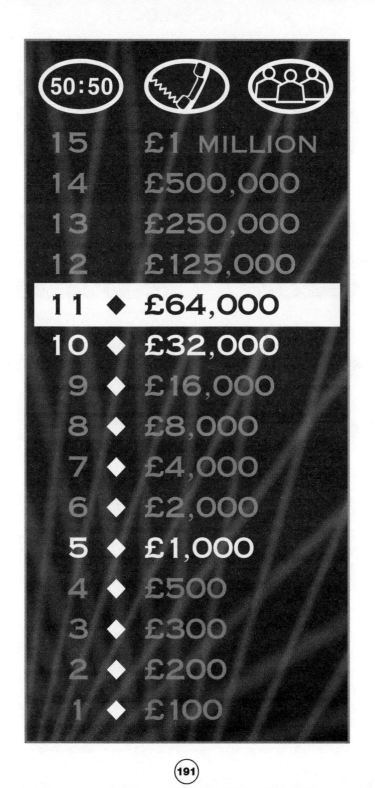

1

In which Charles Dickens novel
does Mrs Pardiggle appear?

A: Our Mutual Friend
B: Bleak House
C: Pickwick Papers
D: Little Dorrit

2

The world's second largest barrier reef
is off the coast of which country?

A: Belize
B: Kenya
C: Dominican Republic
D: Papua New Guinea

3

In which building did Queen Victoria
marry Prince Albert?

A: Windsor Castle
B: Buckingham Palace
C: St James's Palace
D: Westminster Abbey

4

Which of these dances originated in Poland?

A: Waltz
B: Mazurka
C: Polka
D: Jive

5

The game mah-jong takes its name
from the Chinese word meaning what?

A: Sparrows
B: Dragons
C: Ribbons
D: Goldfish

If you would like to use your 50:50 please turn to page 251
Turn to the answer section on page 260 to find out if you've won £64,000!

6

Which country is the world's largest producer of coal?

A: India

B: Russia

C: China

D: USA

7

Which of the following vitamins is also called 'retinol'?

A: Vitamin A

B: Vitamin B_2

C: Vitamin E

D: Vitamin K

8

In 'A Journal of the Plague Year', who described the events of the 1660s?

A: Daniel Defoe

B: Jonathan Swift

C: John Dryden

D: Samuel Pepys

9

The word 'aristocracy' literally means power in the hands of whom?

A: The rich

B: The barons

C: The best

D: The few

10

How many stars are on the flag of New Zealand?

A: Four

B: Five

C: Six

D: Seven

If you would like to use your 50:50 please turn to page 251
Turn to the answer section on page 260 to find out if you've won £64,000!

11

In British greyhound racing, what colour is worn by the dog in trap three?

- A: Red
- B: White
- C: Blue
- D: Black

12

On which river does Baghdad stand?

- A: Tigris
- B: Euphrates
- C: Jordan
- D: Bosporus

13

How are Dominican monks also known?

- A: Whitefriars
- B: Greyfriars
- C: Blackfriars
- D: Trappists

14

What does the letter F indicate on a Plimsoll line?

- A: Fresh water
- B: Full
- C: Freight
- D: Fuel

15

Under what name did Erich Weiss achieve fame?

- A: Harry Houdini
- B: Blondin
- C: Lord Haw Haw
- D: Edward G. Robinson

If you would like to use your 50:50 please turn to page 251
Turn to the answer section on page 260 to find out if you've won £64,000!

16

What does 'pot pourri' literally mean?

- A: Flower power
- B: Pleasant smell
- C: Rotten pot
- D: Clean air

17

What was the name of Rigsby's cat in the TV comedy series 'Rising Damp'?

- A: Vienna
- B: Beethoven
- C: Sofia
- D: Chelsea

18

In which activity are 'jesses' used?

- A: Angling
- B: Hare-coursing
- C: Falconry
- D: Archery

19

If a chemical substance is 'volatile', what is it likely to form?

- A: Acid
- B: Vapour
- C: Compound
- D: Liquid

20

In terms of population, what is the largest Portuguese speaking city in the world?

- A: Lisbon
- B: Rio de Janeiro
- C: Sao Paulo
- D: Oporto

If you would like to use your 50:50 please turn to page 251
Turn to the answer section on page 260 to find out if you've won £64,000!

21

Which garment is secured by a sash called an 'obi'?

- A: Kimono
- B: Sari
- C: Jellaba
- D: Judo robe

22

A 'bibliophile' is someone who enjoys which activity?

- A: Drinking
- B: Travelling
- C: Eating
- D: Reading

23

What was the full first name of gangster Al Capone?

- A: Alan
- B: Alfredo
- C: Alphonse
- D: Alberto

24

What is lithium?

- A: A metal
- B: A gas
- C: A fossil
- D: A rock

25

Which children's author owned Hill Top Farm in the Lake District?

- A: A.A. Milne
- B: Beatrix Potter
- C: Enid Blyton
- D: Roald Dahl

If you would like to use your 50:50 please turn to page 251
Turn to the answer section on page 260 to find out if you've won £64,000!

26

The dunnock is a bird more commonly known by what name?

- A: House martin
- B: Goldfinch
- C: Hedge sparrow
- D: Chaffinch

27

What does it mean when a written phrase is put 'in parenthesis'?

- A: It is enclosed in brackets
- B: It is put in inverted commas
- C: It ends with a question mark
- D: It is put in code

28

Which British prime minister said, 'When I want to read a novel, I write one.'?

- A: Disraeli
- B: Gladstone
- C: Churchill
- D: Palmerston

29

In which mountain range is K2, the second highest mountain in the world?

- A: Karakoram
- B: Himalayas
- C: Hindu Kush
- D: Urals

30

Which salad vegetable belongs to the same family as the poisonous 'deadly nightshade'?

- A: Tomato
- B: Radish
- C: Cucumber
- D: Beetroot

If you would like to use your 50:50 please turn to page 251
Turn to the answer section on page 260 to find out if you've won £64,000!

31

Which musical features the character Nicely-Nicely Johnson?

- A: Gypsy
- B: Carousel
- C: Oklahoma!
- D: Guys and Dolls

32

What sort of creature is Gandalf in J.R.R. Tolkien's novel 'The Hobbit'?

- A: Elf
- B: Dragon
- C: Wizard
- D: Goblin

33

Matt Monro sang the theme to which James Bond film?

- A: Goldfinger
- B: From Russia With Love
- C: Thunderball
- D: Dr. No

34

The first three King Edwards belonged to which Royal House?

- A: Plantagenet
- B: Lancaster
- C: York
- D: Tudor

35

What was the catchphrase of comedian Sandy Powell?

- A: You lucky people!
- B: She knows, you know
- C: Can you hear me, mother?
- D: What a performance!

If you would like to use your 50:50 please turn to page 251
Turn to the answer section on page 260 to find out if you've won £64,000!

36

Which fictional detective first appeared
in the book 'The Mysterious Affair At Styles'?

A: Miss Marple
B: Hercule Poirot
C: Sherlock Holmes
D: Lord Peter Wimsey

37

How many players are there
in a Canadian football team?

A: Eleven
B: Twelve
C: Fifteen
D: Eighteen

38

Which of these countries joined the EC in 1986?

A: Luxembourg
B: Portugal
C: Austria
D: Finland

39

What does 'stegosaurus' mean?

A: Spiny lizard
B: Roof lizard
C: Claw lizard
D: Flat lizard

40

TV presenter Eamonn Andrews was
a former junior champion in which sport?

A: Wrestling
B: Swimming
C: Fencing
D: Boxing

If you would like to use your 50:50 please turn to page 251
Turn to the answer section on page 260 to find out if you've won £64,000!

41

What is the middle name of former US president Jimmy Carter?

A: Lord
B: Baron
C: Earl
D: Duke

42

What was the first bird Noah let out of the Ark?

A: Owl
B: Raven
C: Dove
D: Skylark

43

What was the nickname of jazz saxophonist Charlie Parker?

A: Fish
B: Animal
C: Bird
D: Insect

44

Who was the Greek goddess of victory?

A: Nike
B: Nemesis
C: Victoria
D: Hera

45

How many US states begin with the word 'New'?

A: Four
B: Five
C: Six
D: Seven

If you would like to use your 50:50 please turn to page 251
Turn to the answer section on page 260 to find out if you've won £64,000!

46

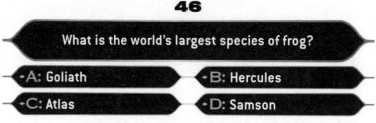

What is the world's largest species of frog?

A: Goliath
B: Hercules
C: Atlas
D: Samson

If you would like to use your 50:50 please turn to page 251
Turn to the answer section on page 260 to find out if you've won £64,000!

1

Which of these Frank Sinatra songs reached the top of the UK pop charts?

- A: Strangers in the Night
- B: My Way
- C: Love and Marriage
- D: High Hopes

2

In which of these disciplines did Vitaly Scherbo not win Olympic gold in 1992?

- A: Floor
- B: Parallel bars
- C: Rings
- D: Pommel horse

3

Which famous actor played the killer of PC Dixon in the film 'The Blue Lamp'?

- A: Dirk Bogarde
- B: Stanley Baker
- C: Jack Warner
- D: Alec Guinness

4

Which poison is obtained from wolf's-bane?

- A: Strychnine
- B: Aconite
- C: Curare
- D: Cyanide

5

In which modern country is the region known in ancient times as Cappadocia?

- A: Greece
- B: Turkey
- C: Bulgaria
- D: Romania

If you would like to use your 50:50 please turn to page 252
Turn to the answer section on page 260 to find out if you've won £125,000!

6

What structure has two basic
types called 'gravity' and 'arch'?

- A: Bridge
- B: Dam
- C: Pier
- D: Road

7

In what field is the Australian Sidney Nolan famous?

- A: Engineering
- B: Ballet
- C: Film
- D: Painting

8

Which creatures gather in groups called 'musters'?

- A: Peacocks
- B: Tigers
- C: Soldier ants
- D: Owls

9

Who created the detective C. Auguste Dupin?

- A: Victor Hugo
- B: Agatha Christie
- C: Wilkie Collins
- D: Edgar Allan Poe

10

In Greek mythology, who was
the god of flocks and herds?

- A: Diana
- B: Hermes
- C: Sylvanus
- D: Pan

If you would like to use your 50:50 please turn to page 252
Turn to the answer section on page 260 to find out if you've won £125,000!

11

Which US state is nicknamed
the 'Mother of Presidents'?

A: Delaware
B: Virginia
C: South Carolina
D: North Dakota

12

Which of these was one of the original 'Cinque Ports'?

A: Winchelsea
B: Hastings
C: Folkestone
D: Rye

13

Who scored six goals in the 1903 FA Cup Final?

A: Bury
B: Derby County
C: Everton
D: Sheffield United

14

Which part of an animal's body
is known as the 'carapace'?

A: Shell
B: Snout
C: Hoof
D: Tail

15

Which term can be used to describe
one tenth of a nautical mile?

A: Furlong
B: Cable
C: Fathom
D: Chain

If you would like to use your 50:50 please turn to page 252
Turn to the answer section on page 260 to find out if you've won £125,000!

16

What was 'Che' Guevara's real first name?

A: Ernesto

B: Alfredo

C: Edmundo

D: Ricardo

17

What is a 'gamp'?

A: Umbrella

B: Fish

C: Lantern

D: Fruit

18

'The Roodee' is a race course in which English city?

A: York

B: Liverpool

C: Durham

D: Chester

19

What can be described as 'Flemish bond' or 'English bond'?

A: Thatched roofs

B: Ploughing styles

C: Arches

D: Brickwork

20

Which TV character had a secretary called Joan Greengross?

A: Jim Bergerac

B: Reginald Perrin

C: James Herriot

D: Mike Baldwin

If you would like to use your 50:50 please turn to page 252
Turn to the answer section on page 260 to find out if you've won £125,000!

21

Of what is gymnophobia the fear?

- A: Nudity
- B: Women
- C: Marriage
- D: Exercise

22

What is a 'filbert'?

- A: Waistcoat
- B: Kilt
- C: Table
- D: Hazelnut

23

What sort of animal is sometimes called a coney?

- A: Raccoon
- B: Rabbit
- C: Skunk
- D: Beaver

24

Which of these is a former name for the Russian city of Volgograd?

- A: Leningrad
- B: St Petersburg
- C: Minsk
- D: Stalingrad

25

Where would a 'peruke' be worn?

- A: On the wrist
- B: Around the neck
- C: On the head
- D: Around the waist

If you would like to use your 50:50 please turn to page 252
Turn to the answer section on page 260 to find out if you've won £125,000!

26

How many degrees are there in an 'octant'?

A: 45
B: 60
C: 75
D: 90

27

In heraldry, what shape is a lozenge?

A: Triangle
B: Diamond
C: Circle
D: Oval

28

What does a numismatist collect?

A: Stamps
B: Fossils
C: Teddy bears
D: Coins

29

What kind of animal is a Peruvian cavy?

A: Rabbit
B: Chinchilla
C: Gerbil
D: Guinea pig

30

In Greek mythology, which nine-headed monster grew two for every one that was chopped off?

A: Hydra
B: Medusa
C: Scylla
D: Medea

If you would like to use your 50:50 please turn to page 252
Turn to the answer section on page 260 to find out if you've won £125,000!

31

Approximately how long is the Panama Canal, linking the Atlantic and Pacific Oceans?

A: 39 miles
B: 51 miles
C: 77 miles
D: 103 miles

32

If a gardener was working with 'scions and stocks', what would he be doing?

A: Cross-pollinating
B: Grafting
C: Germinating hybrids
D: Thinning seedlings

33

In which country is the Lester B Pearson international airport?

A: New Zealand
B: Jamaica
C: South Africa
D: Canada

34

What kind of animal is a 'moke'?

A: Monkey
B: Donkey
C: Sheep
D: Dog

35

'Die, my dear doctor, that's the last thing I shall do' are the reputed last words of which prime minister?

A: William Gladstone
B: Lord Palmerston
C: Benjamin Disraeli
D: Duke of Wellington

If you would like to use your 50:50 please turn to page 252
Turn to the answer section on page 260 to find out if you've won £125,000!

12 ◆ £125,000

36

In American football, who won the
most Super Bowls in the 1980s?

A: Washington Redskins
B: Chicago Bears
C: New York Giants
D: San Francisco 49ers

37

Who married Elizabeth Marchant
de Saint-Michel in 1655?

A: Oliver Cromwell
B: Samuel Pepys
C: Christopher Wren
D: Isaac Newton

38

Which science fiction TV series
featured evil robots called Cylons?

A: Doctor Who
B: Star Trek
C: Space 1999
D: Battlestar Galactica

39

A 'selenograph' is a scientific map of what?

A: Ocean floor
B: Moon
C: Mars
D: Constellations

40

Which of these wives of King Henry VIII was beheaded?

A: Anne of Cleves
B: Catherine Parr
C: Catherine of Aragon
D: Catherine Howard

If you would like to use your 50:50 please turn to page 252
Turn to the answer section on page 260 to find out if you've won £125,000!

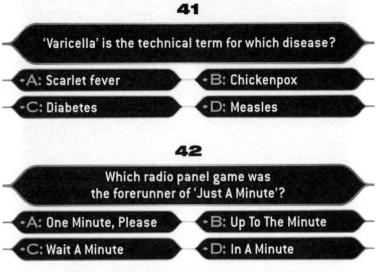

41

'Varicella' is the technical term for which disease?

- A: Scarlet fever
- B: Chickenpox
- C: Diabetes
- D: Measles

42

Which radio panel game was
the forerunner of 'Just A Minute'?

- A: One Minute, Please
- B: Up To The Minute
- C: Wait A Minute
- D: In A Minute

If you would like to use your 50:50 please turn to page 252
Turn to the answer section on page 260 to find out if you've won £125,000!

13 ◆ £250,000

1

Who was the wife of Rembrandt, the subject of many of his portraits?

- A: Monica
- B: Letitia
- C: Saskia
- D: Corinna

2

Which was the first film to feature the on-screen pairing of Spencer Tracy and Katharine Hepburn?

- A: Morning Glory
- B: Adam's Rib
- C: Guess Who's Coming to Dinner?
- D: Woman of the Year

3

Who was awarded the Nobel Peace Prize in 1979?

- A: Desmond Tutu
- B: Amnesty International
- C: The Dalai Lama
- D: Mother Teresa of Calcutta

4

According to the Old Testament, who was the wife of Abraham and mother of Isaac?

- A: Ruth
- B: Miriam
- C: Naomi
- D: Sarah

5

Who wrote the music of the German national anthem?

- A: Josef Haydn
- B: Richard Wagner
- C: Johannes Brahms
- D: Ludwig van Beethoven

If you would like to use your 50:50 please turn to page 253
Turn to the answer section on page 261 to find out if you've won £250,000!

6

'View of Delft' is one of the
best known works by which artist?

- A: Van Dyck
- B: Rembrandt
- C: Van Eyck
- D: Vermeer

7

Where is the largest volcano known to man?

- A: Hawaii
- B: Mars
- C: Peru
- D: Venus

8

In March 1965, who became the
first person to walk in space?

- A: Ed White
- B: Vladimir Komarov
- C: James McDivett
- D: Alexei Leonov

9

In which year was Marie Antoinette,
the wife of Louis XVI of France, executed?

- A: 1791
- B: 1793
- C: 1795
- D: 1797

10

By what name is Haydn's
92nd symphony popularly known?

- A: London
- B: Surprise
- C: Oxford
- D: Clock

If you would like to use your 50:50 please turn to page 253
Turn to the answer section on page 261 to find out if you've won £250,000!

11

What nationality was the astronomer Copernicus?

A: Swedish
B: Dutch
C: Polish
D: Greek

12

Who was the first Republican
president of the United States?

A: John Adams
B: Abraham Lincoln
C: Grover Cleveland
D: Theodore Roosevelt

13

Which part in the original 'Star Wars'
film was played by Peter Mayhew?

A: R2-D2
B: C-3PO
C: Chewbacca
D: Darth Vader

14

Which jockey rode Corbiere to victory
in the 1983 Grand National?

A: Ben De Haan
B: Dick Saunders
C: Hywel Davies
D: Richard Dunwoody

15

In which of these years was a
total eclipse of the sun visible in Britain?

A: 1927
B: 1933
C: 1939
D: 1946

If you would like to use your 50:50 please turn to page 253
Turn to the answer section on page 261 to find out if you've won £250,000!

16

Which of these paper sizes is the smallest?

A: Atlas

B: Foolscap

C: Demy

D: Medium

17

Published in 1975, 'Grimus' is the
first novel by which author?

A: Melvyn Bragg

B: Salman Rushdie

C: Peter Carey

D: Stephen King

18

The king and crown prince of which country were
assassinated on the same day in 1908?

A: Italy

B: Portugal

C: Greece

D: Romania

19

Which of these waves have the shortest wavelength?

A: Gamma rays

B: X-rays

C: Ultraviolet waves

D: Infrared waves

20

Who was prime minister when
Captain Scott reached the South Pole?

A: Lloyd George

B: Campbell-Bannerman

C: Bonar Law

D: Asquith

If you would like to use your 50:50 please turn to page 253
Turn to the answer section on page 261 to find out if you've won £250,000!

13 ◆ £250,000

21

How many satellites has the planet Uranus?

- A: Nine
- B: Eleven
- C: Thirteen
- D: Fifteen

22

Which country's international car registration is DZ?

- A: Belize
- B: Benin
- C: Algeria
- D: Madagascar

23

What would a person suffering from 'sitophobia' fear?

- A: Glass
- B: Pins
- C: Food
- D: Hair

24

With which of these composers did the female French novelist George Sand have an affair?

- A: Bizet
- B: Berlioz
- C: Chopin
- D: Debussy

25

What was the title of Graham Greene's first novel?

- A: Stamboul Train
- B: The Man Within
- C: It's A Battlefield
- D: England Made Me

If you would like to use your 50:50 please turn to page 253
Turn to the answer section on page 261 to find out if you've won £250,000!

26

Which knight of the Round Table fought a mysterious Green Knight?

A: Sir Lancelot
B: Sir Gawain
C: Sir Percival
D: Sir Galahad

27

Which element has the chemical symbol Cm?

A: Caesium
B: Cadmium
C: Chromium
D: Curium

28

In Shakespeare's 'Hamlet', who is Ophelia's father?

A: Laertes
B: Claudius
C: Polonius
D: Horatio

29

Which author helped to develop the Bow Street Runners, an early police force?

A: Jonathan Swift
B: Henry Fielding
C: Anthony Trollope
D: Charles Dickens

30

'Cinnabar' is the only commercially useful ore of which metal?

A: Zinc
B: Iron
C: Tin
D: Mercury

If you would like to use your 50:50 please turn to page 253
Turn to the answer section on page 261 to find out if you've won £250,000!

31

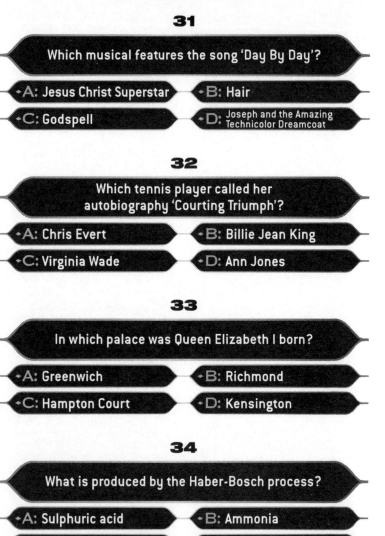

Which musical features the song 'Day By Day'?

- A: Jesus Christ Superstar
- B: Hair
- C: Godspell
- D: Joseph and the Amazing Technicolor Dreamcoat

32

Which tennis player called her autobiography 'Courting Triumph'?

- A: Chris Evert
- B: Billie Jean King
- C: Virginia Wade
- D: Ann Jones

33

In which palace was Queen Elizabeth I born?

- A: Greenwich
- B: Richmond
- C: Hampton Court
- D: Kensington

34

What is produced by the Haber-Bosch process?

- A: Sulphuric acid
- B: Ammonia
- C: PVC
- D: Stainless Steel

35

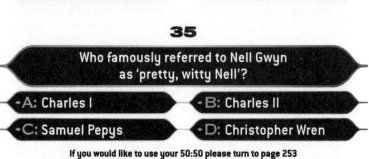

Who famously referred to Nell Gwyn as 'pretty, witty Nell'?

- A: Charles I
- B: Charles II
- C: Samuel Pepys
- D: Christopher Wren

If you would like to use your 50:50 please turn to page 253
Turn to the answer section on page 261 to find out if you've won £250,000!

13 ◆ £250,000

36

Who wrote 'The History of the World'
while imprisoned in the Tower of London?

◆A: Lady Jane Grey ◆B: Thomas More
◆C: Walter Raleigh ◆D: Mary, Queen of Scots

37

What is the name for the study
of fossil pollen and spores?

◆A: Palynology ◆B: Muscology
◆C: Palaeopedology ◆D: Graminology

38

In the 1960s, which designer created
the 'Space Age' collection?

◆A: Mary Quant ◆B: Pierre Cardin
◆C: Yves Saint Laurent ◆D: Vivienne Westwood

If you would like to use your 50:50 please turn to page 253
Turn to the answer section on page 261 to find out if you've won £250,000!

14 ◆ £500,000

1

Karl Landsteiner won a Nobel Prize
for his discovery of what?

- A: Blood groups
- B: Smallpox vaccine
- C: DNA
- D: Insulin

2

Which country has a new parliament
building known as the 'Beehive'?

- A: Australia
- B: Canada
- C: Ireland
- D: New Zealand

3

Which team won the first Scottish FA Cup final?

- A: Dundee
- B: Rangers
- C: Queen's Park
- D: Vale of Leven

4

What is the name of the highest
waterfall in North America?

- A: Niagara
- B: Horseshoe
- C: Yosemite
- D: Ribbon

5

What name did the artist Michelangelo Merisi adopt?

- A: Correggio
- B: Titian
- C: Botticelli
- D: Caravaggio

If you would like to use your 50:50 please turn to page 253
Turn to the answer section on page 261 to find out if you've won £500,000!

6

What kind of bridge is the Golden Gate Bridge?

A: Cantilever | B: Bascule

C: Suspension | D: Steel arch

7

In heraldry, which family member is denoted by a rose?

A: Wife | B: Eldest son

C: Seventh son | D: Daughter

8

Which stage musical features the song 'Something To Dance About'?

A: Pal Joey | B: Call Me Madam

C: Face The Music | D: No, No, Nanette

9

Which river rises near Lake Baikal and flows to the Laptev Sea?

A: Lena | B: Volga

C: Ob | D: Yenisey

10

In which Dickens novel do the Cheeryble Brothers appear?

A: Nicholas Nickleby | B: Pickwick Papers

C: Our Mutual Friend | D: Hard Times

If you would like to use your 50:50 please turn to page 253
Turn to the answer section on page 261 to find out if you've won £500,000!

14 ◆ £500,000

11

From which author's work did scientists take the word 'quark'?

- A: Lewis Carroll
- B: Edward Lear
- C: James Joyce
- D: Aldous Huxley

12

What is 'phylloxera'?

- A: Lung infection
- B: Insect
- C: Shrub
- D: Green pigment

13

How many different combinations of dots are used in Braille?

- A: 49
- B: 63
- C: 75
- D: 87

14

Which country's highest point is Mount Korab?

- A: Albania
- B: Jordan
- C: Belarus
- D: Morocco

15

What sort of creature is a 'swartback'?

- A: Pig
- B: Duck
- C: Gull
- D: Goose

If you would like to use your 50:50 please turn to page 253
Turn to the answer section on page 261 to find out if you've won £500,000!

14 ♦ £500,000

16

On what would you see a 'gnomon'?

A: Sundial
B: Cliff face
C: Yacht
D: Tree

17

On which of these would you find a 'hame'?

A: Suit of armour
B: Rowing boat
C: Horse's harness
D: Spinning wheel

18

Which city is home to the 8th century 'Book of Kells'?

A: Edinburgh
B: London
C: Oxford
D: Dublin

19

Which family fought the Earp brothers at the OK Corral?

A: The Clantons
B: The Clintons
C: The Cliftons
D: The Graftons

20

Which English king was known as 'Old Rowley'?

A: Henry VIII
B: Richard III
C: Charles II
D: George IV

If you would like to use your 50:50 please turn to page 253
Turn to the answer section on page 261 to find out if you've won £500,000!

21

The Queen Alexandra's birdwing, the world's largest butterfly, is native to which island?

- A: Bali
- B: Borneo
- C: Madagascar
- D: New Guinea

22

Which horse won the 2000 Guineas, the Derby and the St Leger in 1970?

- A: Pinza
- B: Nijinsky
- C: The Minstrel
- D: Mill Reef

23

Who lived at Hughenden Manor in Buckinghamshire?

- A: Charles Dickens
- B: Benjamin Disraeli
- C: William Gladstone
- D: Thomas Hardy

24

Which of these geological periods came first?

- A: Cretaceous
- B: Devonian
- C: Silurian
- D: Triassic

25

Which of these British prime ministers was educated at Harrow School?

- A: William Gladstone
- B: Duke of Wellington
- C: Harold Macmillan
- D: Robert Peel

If you would like to use your 50:50 please turn to page 253
Turn to the answer section on page 261 to find out if you've won £500,000!

26

What was the native language of Jesus Christ?

- A: Aramaic
- B: Arabic
- C: Sanskrit
- D: Hebrew

27

The Somerset Maugham novel
'The Moon and Sixpence' is set on which island?

- A: Cuba
- B: Isle of Wight
- C: Madeira
- D: Tahiti

28

Which of these elements is
contained in a strip-lighting tube?

- A: Mercury
- B: Cobalt
- C: Sodium
- D: Carbon

29

In which of these countries
could you spend a 'centavo'?

- A: Uruguay
- B: Peru
- C: Bolivia
- D: Venezuela

30

'How Long's the Course?' is the
autobiography of which athlete?

- A: Linford Christie
- B: Diane Modahl
- C: Roger Black
- D: Colin Jackson

If you would like to use your 50:50 please turn to page 253
Turn to the answer section on page 261 to find out if you've won £500,000!

31

By area, which is the largest of these English counties?

A: Kent

B: Hampshire

C: Essex

D: Cornwall

32

Who was prime minister at the time of the Boston Tea Party?

A: William Pitt

B: Earl of Shelburne

C: Henry Addington

D: Lord North

33

What is the name of the largest asteroid in the Solar System?

A: Ceres

B: Pallas

C: Hygeia

D: Vesta

34

On which date in October 1929 was 'Black Thursday', the day the Wall Street Crash began?

A: 24th

B: 25th

C: 28th

D: 29th

If you would like to use your 50:50 please turn to page 253
Turn to the answer section on page 261 to find out if you've won £500,000!

15 ♦ £1,000,000

1

Ginger Rogers won a Best Actress Oscar
for the film 'Kitty Foyle', released in which year?

- A: 1934
- B: 1936
- C: 1938
- D: 1940

2

Which of these members of the
Royal Family was born in 1961?

- A: Earl of Wessex
- B: Lady Helen Taylor
- C: Duke of York
- D: Viscount Linley

3

The Four Noble Truths are central to which religion?

- A: Buddhism
- B: Islam
- C: Hinduism
- D: Judaism

4

What name is given to an
inhabitant of the city of Sydney?

- A: Sydneysider
- B: Sydovian
- C: Sydneyphile
- D: Sydite

5

Where did the golfer Tom Watson
win his first British Open?

- A: Carnoustie
- B: Muirfield
- C: Royal Birkdale
- D: Turnberry

If you would like to use your 50:50 please turn to page 254
Turn to the answer section on page 261 to find out if you've won £1,000,000!

6

What is the SI unit of magnetic flux density?

- A: Farad
- B: Tesla
- C: Maxwell
- D: Henry

7

What is the title of the third part of T.S. Eliot's poem 'The Waste Land'?

- A: A Game of Chess
- B: Death by Water
- C: What the Thunder Said
- D: The Fire Sermon

8

Which planet has a moon called Larissa?

- A: Jupiter
- B: Saturn
- C: Uranus
- D: Neptune

9

In heraldry, what does 'addorsed' mean?

- A: Lying down
- B: Sitting up
- C: Back to back
- D: Side by side

10

The fall in pitch of a vehicle's siren as it passes is associated with which scientist?

- A: Corioli
- B: Newton
- C: Doppler
- D: Hooke

If you would like to use your 50:50 please turn to page 254
Turn to the answer section on page 261 to find out if you've won £1,000,000!

15 ◆ £1,000,000

11

'Hydroponics' is a term related
to which of the following?

- A: Whale song
- B: Plant growing
- C: Sea travel
- D: Humidity measurement

12

Which classic radio comedy series featured
Maurice Denham as charlady Lola Tickle?

- A: ITMA
- B: Educating Archie
- C: Take It From Here
- D: Much-Binding-in-the-Marsh

13

Which Hollywood star made an early appearance
in the 1984 film 'BMX Bandits'?

- A: Michelle Pfeiffer
- B: Julia Roberts
- C: Nicole Kidman
- D: Meg Ryan

14

Sir Seretse Khama was the first
president of which country?

- A: Botswana
- B: Tanzania
- C: Ghana
- D: Zambia

15

Which decimal number is equal
to the binary number 10?

- A: Ten
- B: Two
- C: One
- D: Three

If you would like to use your 50:50 please turn to page 254
Turn to the answer section on page 261 to find out if you've won £1,000,000!

16

What is the English name for
the Jewish festival of Pesach?

A: New Year
B: Day of Atonement
C: Feast of Tabernacles
D: Passover

17

Which star type has the hottest surface temperature?

A: White
B: Red
C: Blue
D: Yellow

18

Which of these islands was ruled by
Britain from 1815 until 1864?

A: Crete
B: Cyprus
C: Corsica
D: Corfu

19

Which of these colours does not
appear on the national flag of Lithuania?

A: Blue
B: Yellow
C: Red
D: Green

20

Boadicea's tribe, the Iceni,
lived in which part of Britain?

A: Northumberland
B: East Anglia
C: Wales
D: Cornwall

If you would like to use your 50:50 please turn to page 254
Turn to the answer section on page 261 to find out if you've won £1,000,000!

15 ◆ £1,000,000

21

In which Canadian province is Uranium City?

- A: Alberta
- B: Saskatchewan
- C: Manitoba
- D: British Columbia

22

Which of these is not a mineral used on the Mohs scale of hardness?

- A: Orthoclase
- B: Apatite
- C: Graphite
- D: Gypsum

23

The word 'emmet' is an archaic term for which creature?

- A: Ant
- B: Newt
- C: Young hawk
- D: Worm

24

On average, which is the smallest thrush found in Britain?

- A: Ring ouzel
- B: Redwing
- C: Song thrush
- D: Blackbird

25

Who was nicknamed 'The Sailor King'?

- A: Henry VIII
- B: George III
- C: Charles II
- D: William IV

If you would like to use your 50:50 please turn to page 254
Turn to the answer section on page 261 to find out if you've won £1,000,000!

15 ◆ £1,000,000

26

In which country is the city of Bukhara?

- A: Uzbekistan
- B: Turkmenistan
- C: Kazakhstan
- D: Tajikistan

27

Which cartoon character made his screen debut in 1935?

- A: Porky Pig
- B: Popeye
- C: Pluto
- D: Bugs Bunny

28

Which of these words refers to land endowed to a parish church?

- A: Glebe
- B: Demesne
- C: Pannage
- D: Fiefdom

29

If an object is described as 'hastate', what does it resemble in shape?

- A: Bunch of grapes
- B: Pouch
- C: Spearhead
- D: Doughnut

30

Which bird has a display flight called 'roding'?

- A: Woodcock
- B: Snipe
- C: Ruff
- D: Nightjar

If you would like to use your 50:50 please turn to page 254
Turn to the answer section on page 261 to find out if you've won £1,000,000!

50:50

£100

1	options remaining are A & B	38	options remaining are A & C
2	options remaining are B & C	39	options remaining are A & B
3	options remaining are A & B	40	options remaining are A & D
4	options remaining are A & B	41	options remaining are A & D
5	options remaining are B & C	42	options remaining are B & C
6	options remaining are A & C	43	options remaining are B & D
7	options remaining are A & C	44	options remaining are C & D
8	options remaining are B & D	45	options remaining are B & D
9	options remaining are A & C	46	options remaining are A & C
10	options remaining are B & D	47	options remaining are A & B
11	options remaining are C & D	48	options remaining are B & D
12	options remaining are A & C	49	options remaining are A & B
13	options remaining are A & C	50	options remaining are A & D
14	options remaining are A & B	51	options remaining are A & B
15	options remaining are B & C	52	options remaining are B & C
16	options remaining are B & C	53	options remaining are A & B
17	options remaining are A & B	54	options remaining are C & D
18	options remaining are A & C	55	options remaining are A & D
19	options remaining are A & C	56	options remaining are C & D
20	options remaining are A & B	57	options remaining are C & D
21	options remaining are A & B	58	options remaining are A & B
22	options remaining are A & B	59	options remaining are A & B
23	options remaining are A & B	60	options remaining are C & D
24	options remaining are B & C	61	options remaining are C & D
25	options remaining are B & C	62	options remaining are A & C
26	options remaining are A & D	63	options remaining are B & C
27	options remaining are A & C	64	options remaining are A & B
28	options remaining are A & D	65	options remaining are A & D
29	options remaining are A & C	66	options remaining are B & D
30	options remaining are B & D	67	options remaining are A & C
31	options remaining are B & C	68	options remaining are B & D
32	options remaining are A & C	69	options remaining are A & C
33	options remaining are B & D	70	options remaining are A & B
34	options remaining are A & C	71	options remaining are A & C
35	options remaining are A & C	72	options remaining are C & D
36	options remaining are B & D	73	options remaining are A & C
37	options remaining are A & D	74	options remaining are A & B

50:50

£200

50:50

43	options remaining are A & C	85	options remaining are A & B
44	options remaining are B & C	86	options remaining are A & C
45	options remaining are C & D	87	options remaining are C & D
46	options remaining are A & D	88	options remaining are A & C
47	options remaining are A & B	89	options remaining are A & C
48	options remaining are C & D	90	options remaining are B & D
49	options remaining are B & D	91	options remaining are B & D
50	options remaining are B & D	92	options remaining are A & D
51	options remaining are B & C	93	options remaining are A & C
52	options remaining are A & B	94	options remaining are C & D
53	options remaining are A & C	95	options remaining are A & B
54	options remaining are C & D	96	options remaining are A & D
55	options remaining are A & D	97	options remaining are A & B
56	options remaining are A & C	98	options remaining are B & D
57	options remaining are A & B		
58	options remaining are A & D		
59	options remaining are B & D		
60	options remaining are A & C		
61	options remaining are A & B		
62	options remaining are A & D		
63	options remaining are B & D		
64	options remaining are A & C		
65	options remaining are B & C		
66	options remaining are B & C		
67	options remaining are B & D		
68	options remaining are B & C		
69	options remaining are A & D		
70	options remaining are A & C		
71	options remaining are B & C		
72	options remaining are B & D		
73	options remaining are A & B		
74	options remaining are A & C		
75	options remaining are A & D		
76	options remaining are A & D		
77	options remaining are C & D		
78	options remaining are A & C		
79	options remaining are C & D		
80	options remaining are A & D		
81	options remaining are A & D		
82	options remaining are A & B		
83	options remaining are A & C		
84	options remaining are A & B		

50:50

£300

1	options remaining are B & C	43	options remaining are B & C
2	options remaining are A & C	44	options remaining are B & C
3	options remaining are A & C	45	options remaining are B & C
4	options remaining are A & C	46	options remaining are A & C
5	options remaining are A & B	47	options remaining are B & D
6	options remaining are A & D	48	options remaining are B & C
7	options remaining are A & D	49	options remaining are B & D
8	options remaining are A & D	50	options remaining are A & C
9	options remaining are A & C	51	options remaining are C & D
10	options remaining are A & D	52	options remaining are C & D
11	options remaining are A & B	53	options remaining are A & B
12	options remaining are A & C	54	options remaining are A & B
13	options remaining are A & D	55	options remaining are B & C
14	options remaining are A & C	56	options remaining are C & D
15	options remaining are A & B	57	options remaining are A & B
16	options remaining are A & C	58	options remaining are A & B
17	options remaining are A & B	59	options remaining are A & B
18	options remaining are A & D	60	options remaining are B & D
19	options remaining are A & B	61	options remaining are C & D
20	options remaining are A & D	62	options remaining are B & D
21	options remaining are B & D	63	options remaining are A & D
22	options remaining are C & D	64	options remaining are B & C
23	options remaining are B & D	65	options remaining are A & D
24	options remaining are A & B	66	options remaining are A & C
25	options remaining are B & C	67	options remaining are A & B
26	options remaining are B & D	68	options remaining are C & D
27	options remaining are B & C	69	options remaining are A & D
28	options remaining are B & C	70	options remaining are B & C
29	options remaining are B & D	71	options remaining are A & B
30	options remaining are A & B	72	options remaining are B & D
31	options remaining are A & C	73	options remaining are C & D
32	options remaining are B & C	74	options remaining are B & D
33	options remaining are A & D	75	options remaining are B & D
34	options remaining are B & D	76	options remaining are A & B
35	options remaining are C & D	77	options remaining are A & D
36	options remaining are B & C	78	options remaining are B & D
37	options remaining are A & D	79	options remaining are C & D
38	options remaining are B & D	80	options remaining are A & B
39	options remaining are B & C	81	options remaining are A & B
40	options remaining are A & B	82	options remaining are A & B
41	options remaining are A & B	83	options remaining are C & D
42	options remaining are B & D	84	options remaining are A & D

50:50

85	options remaining are B & D
86	options remaining are B & C
87	options remaining are B & C
88	options remaining are A & B
89	options remaining are B & C
90	options remaining are A & D
91	options remaining are B & D
92	options remaining are B & C
93	options remaining are B & D
94	options remaining are B & C

£500

1	options remaining are A & D
2	options remaining are A & D
3	options remaining are A & D
4	options remaining are A & C
5	options remaining are A & C
6	options remaining are A & C
7	options remaining are A & B
8	options remaining are A & B
9	options remaining are B & C
10	options remaining are A & C
11	options remaining are A & C
12	options remaining are A & D
13	options remaining are A & B
14	options remaining are A & C
15	options remaining are A & D
16	options remaining are B & C
17	options remaining are C & D
18	options remaining are B & C
19	options remaining are B & C
20	options remaining are C & D
21	options remaining are A & B
22	options remaining are A & D
23	options remaining are A & C
24	options remaining are A & B
25	options remaining are A & D
26	options remaining are A & B
27	options remaining are B & C
28	options remaining are A & D
29	options remaining are A & B
30	options remaining are B & D
31	options remaining are A & D
32	options remaining are A & D
33	options remaining are B & C
34	options remaining are A & B
35	options remaining are A & B
36	options remaining are B & C
37	options remaining are A & B
38	options remaining are A & B
39	options remaining are A & B
40	options remaining are A & D
41	options remaining are A & D
42	options remaining are B & D

43	options remaining are B & D
44	options remaining are B & C
45	options remaining are A & D
46	options remaining are A & C
47	options remaining are B & C
48	options remaining are B & C
49	options remaining are A & B
50	options remaining are B & D
51	options remaining are B & D
52	options remaining are B & D
53	options remaining are A & C
54	options remaining are B & C
55	options remaining are A & B
56	options remaining are B & D
57	options remaining are B & C
58	options remaining are A & C
59	options remaining are B & C
60	options remaining are A & C
61	options remaining are B & C
62	options remaining are A & B
63	options remaining are C & D
64	options remaining are B & C
65	options remaining are A & D
66	options remaining are A & B
67	options remaining are A & D
68	options remaining are C & D
69	options remaining are B & C
70	options remaining are A & B
71	options remaining are A & C
72	options remaining are B & D
73	options remaining are A & B
74	options remaining are A & D
75	options remaining are B & D
76	options remaining are C & D
77	options remaining are A & C
78	options remaining are A & B
79	options remaining are A & C
80	options remaining are B & C
81	options remaining are A & C
82	options remaining are A & D
83	options remaining are B & D
84	options remaining are C & D
85	options remaining are B & C
86	options remaining are C & D
87	options remaining are B & C
88	options remaining are A & C
89	options remaining are C & D
90	options remaining are B & D

50:50

£1,000

1	options remaining are B & D	43	options remaining are A & D
2	options remaining are C & D	44	options remaining are C & D
3	options remaining are B & D	45	options remaining are A & C
4	options remaining are A & D	46	options remaining are C & D
5	options remaining are A & B	47	options remaining are A & B
6	options remaining are B & C	48	options remaining are A & C
7	options remaining are B & C	49	options remaining are A & D
8	options remaining are A & C	50	options remaining are A & C
9	options remaining are C & D	51	options remaining are A & B
10	options remaining are A & C	52	options remaining are B & C
11	options remaining are B & C	53	options remaining are A & C
12	options remaining are A & C	54	options remaining are A & C
13	options remaining are B & C	55	options remaining are A & B
14	options remaining are B & D	56	options remaining are A & D
15	options remaining are A & D	57	options remaining are A & B
16	options remaining are B & D	58	options remaining are B & D
17	options remaining are A & C	59	options remaining are A & D
18	options remaining are B & D	60	options remaining are A & D
19	options remaining are B & C	61	options remaining are B & C
20	options remaining are B & C	62	options remaining are A & B
21	options remaining are B & D	63	options remaining are A & C
22	options remaining are B & D	64	options remaining are A & B
23	options remaining are B & C	65	options remaining are B & C
24	options remaining are B & D	66	options remaining are A & B
25	options remaining are B & D	67	options remaining are B & D
26	options remaining are A & B	68	options remaining are C & D
27	options remaining are B & D	69	options remaining are A & D
28	options remaining are C & D	70	options remaining are A & B
29	options remaining are C & D	71	options remaining are A & D
30	options remaining are C & D	72	options remaining are A & D
31	options remaining are B & D	73	options remaining are A & B
32	options remaining are B & C	74	options remaining are A & B
33	options remaining are A & D	75	options remaining are C & D
34	options remaining are B & C	76	options remaining are C & D
35	options remaining are A & B	77	options remaining are B & C
36	options remaining are C & D	78	options remaining are A & B
37	options remaining are C & D	79	options remaining are B & D
38	options remaining are B & C	80	options remaining are A & B
39	options remaining are A & D	81	options remaining are A & D
40	options remaining are B & D	82	options remaining are A & B
41	options remaining are A & C	83	options remaining are C & D
42	options remaining are B & D	84	options remaining are A & D

50:50

85	options remaining are B & C
86	options remaining are B & C

£2,000

1	options remaining are A & C
2	options remaining are C & D
3	options remaining are A & D
4	options remaining are C & D
5	options remaining are B & C
6	options remaining are A & D
7	options remaining are B & D
8	options remaining are B & D
9	options remaining are B & C
10	options remaining are A & C
11	options remaining are A & B
12	options remaining are B & C
13	options remaining are B & C
14	options remaining are A & C
15	options remaining are A & B
16	options remaining are B & D
17	options remaining are A & C
18	options remaining are A & D
19	options remaining are A & C
20	options remaining are A & B
21	options remaining are C & D
22	options remaining are A & B
23	options remaining are B & D
24	options remaining are C & D
25	options remaining are A & C
26	options remaining are B & C
27	options remaining are A & C
28	options remaining are B & C
29	options remaining are A & C
30	options remaining are A & B
31	options remaining are C & D
32	options remaining are A & D
33	options remaining are A & B
34	options remaining are A & C
35	options remaining are A & C
36	options remaining are A & B
37	options remaining are B & D
38	options remaining are B & D
39	options remaining are B & C
40	options remaining are B & C
41	options remaining are C & D
42	options remaining are B & C

50:50

£4,000

43 options remaining are B & D	1 options remaining are A & D
44 options remaining are B & C	2 options remaining are A & C
45 options remaining are C & D	3 options remaining are B & D
46 options remaining are B & D	4 options remaining are A & D
47 options remaining are B & D	5 options remaining are B & C
48 options remaining are A & C	6 options remaining are A & D
49 options remaining are A & D	7 options remaining are B & C
50 options remaining are B & D	8 options remaining are A & D
51 options remaining are A & D	9 options remaining are A & B
52 options remaining are A & D	10 options remaining are B & C
53 options remaining are B & D	11 options remaining are C & D
54 options remaining are A & C	12 options remaining are A & B
55 options remaining are A & B	13 options remaining are B & D
56 options remaining are B & C	14 options remaining are A & B
57 options remaining are A & C	15 options remaining are B & C
58 options remaining are A & B	16 options remaining are A & B
59 options remaining are A & D	17 options remaining are B & C
60 options remaining are C & D	18 options remaining are B & D
61 options remaining are C & D	19 options remaining are A & D
62 options remaining are A & C	20 options remaining are B & C
63 options remaining are A & B	21 options remaining are B & D
64 options remaining are A & C	22 options remaining are A & B
65 options remaining are C & D	23 options remaining are A & B
66 options remaining are A & D	24 options remaining are A & D
67 options remaining are B & D	25 options remaining are B & D
68 options remaining are B & C	26 options remaining are A & B
69 options remaining are B & C	27 options remaining are B & C
70 options remaining are C & D	28 options remaining are B & D
71 options remaining are B & D	29 options remaining are A & C
72 options remaining are B & D	30 options remaining are C & D
73 options remaining are B & C	31 options remaining are B & C
74 options remaining are A & C	32 options remaining are C & D
	33 options remaining are B & D
	34 options remaining are A & B
	35 options remaining are C & D
	36 options remaining are B & D
	37 options remaining are A & D
	38 options remaining are A & C
	39 options remaining are A & B
	40 options remaining are B & D
	41 options remaining are A & D
	42 options remaining are B & D

50:50

<table>
<tr><td>43</td><td>options remaining are A & D</td></tr>
<tr><td>44</td><td>options remaining are A & B</td></tr>
<tr><td>45</td><td>options remaining are A & C</td></tr>
<tr><td>46</td><td>options remaining are A & D</td></tr>
<tr><td>47</td><td>options remaining are A & D</td></tr>
<tr><td>48</td><td>options remaining are A & B</td></tr>
<tr><td>49</td><td>options remaining are C & D</td></tr>
<tr><td>50</td><td>options remaining are A & B</td></tr>
<tr><td>51</td><td>options remaining are C & D</td></tr>
<tr><td>52</td><td>options remaining are A & B</td></tr>
<tr><td>53</td><td>options remaining are A & B</td></tr>
<tr><td>54</td><td>options remaining are A & D</td></tr>
<tr><td>55</td><td>options remaining are B & C</td></tr>
<tr><td>56</td><td>options remaining are A & D</td></tr>
<tr><td>57</td><td>options remaining are A & C</td></tr>
<tr><td>58</td><td>options remaining are A & C</td></tr>
<tr><td>59</td><td>options remaining are B & C</td></tr>
<tr><td>60</td><td>options remaining are B & D</td></tr>
<tr><td>61</td><td>options remaining are A & B</td></tr>
<tr><td>62</td><td>options remaining are B & C</td></tr>
<tr><td>63</td><td>options remaining are A & D</td></tr>
<tr><td>64</td><td>options remaining are C & D</td></tr>
<tr><td>65</td><td>options remaining are A & B</td></tr>
<tr><td>66</td><td>options remaining are A & B</td></tr>
<tr><td>67</td><td>options remaining are A & C</td></tr>
<tr><td>68</td><td>options remaining are A & D</td></tr>
<tr><td>69</td><td>options remaining are A & C</td></tr>
<tr><td>70</td><td>options remaining are B & D</td></tr>
</table>

£8,000

<table>
<tr><td>1</td><td>options remaining are A & B</td></tr>
<tr><td>2</td><td>options remaining are C & D</td></tr>
<tr><td>3</td><td>options remaining are A & B</td></tr>
<tr><td>4</td><td>options remaining are B & C</td></tr>
<tr><td>5</td><td>options remaining are A & C</td></tr>
<tr><td>6</td><td>options remaining are A & D</td></tr>
<tr><td>7</td><td>options remaining are A & D</td></tr>
<tr><td>8</td><td>options remaining are B & C</td></tr>
<tr><td>9</td><td>options remaining are A & B</td></tr>
<tr><td>10</td><td>options remaining are C & D</td></tr>
<tr><td>11</td><td>options remaining are C & D</td></tr>
<tr><td>12</td><td>options remaining are A & C</td></tr>
<tr><td>13</td><td>options remaining are A & B</td></tr>
<tr><td>14</td><td>options remaining are A & B</td></tr>
<tr><td>15</td><td>options remaining are A & B</td></tr>
<tr><td>16</td><td>options remaining are B & D</td></tr>
<tr><td>17</td><td>options remaining are A & C</td></tr>
<tr><td>18</td><td>options remaining are B & C</td></tr>
<tr><td>19</td><td>options remaining are B & C</td></tr>
<tr><td>20</td><td>options remaining are A & D</td></tr>
<tr><td>21</td><td>options remaining are A & D</td></tr>
<tr><td>22</td><td>options remaining are B & C</td></tr>
<tr><td>23</td><td>options remaining are C & D</td></tr>
<tr><td>24</td><td>options remaining are A & D</td></tr>
<tr><td>25</td><td>options remaining are A & B</td></tr>
<tr><td>26</td><td>options remaining are A & C</td></tr>
<tr><td>27</td><td>options remaining are A & D</td></tr>
<tr><td>28</td><td>options remaining are A & D</td></tr>
<tr><td>29</td><td>options remaining are A & D</td></tr>
<tr><td>30</td><td>options remaining are A & B</td></tr>
<tr><td>31</td><td>options remaining are A & B</td></tr>
<tr><td>32</td><td>options remaining are C & D</td></tr>
<tr><td>33</td><td>options remaining are A & D</td></tr>
<tr><td>34</td><td>options remaining are A & D</td></tr>
<tr><td>35</td><td>options remaining are A & D</td></tr>
<tr><td>36</td><td>options remaining are A & D</td></tr>
<tr><td>37</td><td>options remaining are C & D</td></tr>
<tr><td>38</td><td>options remaining are A & B</td></tr>
<tr><td>39</td><td>options remaining are C & D</td></tr>
<tr><td>40</td><td>options remaining are A & D</td></tr>
<tr><td>41</td><td>options remaining are A & C</td></tr>
<tr><td>42</td><td>options remaining are A & B</td></tr>
</table>

50:50

£16,000

43	options remaining are A & C
44	options remaining are B & C
45	options remaining are B & D
46	options remaining are A & D
47	options remaining are A & C
48	options remaining are A & C
49	options remaining are A & B
50	options remaining are B & D
51	options remaining are B & D
52	options remaining are A & D
53	options remaining are B & D
54	options remaining are A & B
55	options remaining are C & D
56	options remaining are B & C
57	options remaining are A & C
58	options remaining are A & B
59	options remaining are A & C
60	options remaining are A & D
61	options remaining are A & D
62	options remaining are B & C
63	options remaining are A & B
64	options remaining are A & B
65	options remaining are A & B
66	options remaining are A & C

1	options remaining are A & D
2	options remaining are A & C
3	options remaining are A & B
4	options remaining are B & C
5	options remaining are A & D
6	options remaining are C & D
7	options remaining are B & D
8	options remaining are B & C
9	options remaining are A & B
10	options remaining are A & B
11	options remaining are B & D
12	options remaining are A & C
13	options remaining are A & C
14	options remaining are B & C
15	options remaining are B & D
16	options remaining are B & C
17	options remaining are A & B
18	options remaining are A & B
19	options remaining are A & D
20	options remaining are A & B
21	options remaining are B & D
22	options remaining are A & B
23	options remaining are B & C
24	options remaining are A & B
25	options remaining are A & B
26	options remaining are B & C
27	options remaining are B & D
28	options remaining are B & C
29	options remaining are A & B
30	options remaining are A & D
31	options remaining are A & D
32	options remaining are A & C
33	options remaining are A & C
34	options remaining are A & D
35	options remaining are A & C
36	options remaining are A & D
37	options remaining are A & B
38	options remaining are B & C
39	options remaining are B & D
40	options remaining are B & C
41	options remaining are A & C
42	options remaining are A & D

50:50

43 options remaining are A & D	1 options remaining are B & C
44 options remaining are A & B	2 options remaining are A & D
45 options remaining are A & B	3 options remaining are B & C
46 options remaining are B & C	4 options remaining are B & D
47 options remaining are B & C	5 options remaining are A & D
48 options remaining are A & B	6 options remaining are B & D
49 options remaining are C & D	7 options remaining are B & D
50 options remaining are C & D	8 options remaining are A & D
51 options remaining are A & B	9 options remaining are A & D
52 options remaining are A & B	10 options remaining are B & D
53 options remaining are A & D	11 options remaining are B & C
54 options remaining are A & D	12 options remaining are B & C
55 options remaining are B & C	13 options remaining are C & D
56 options remaining are C & D	14 options remaining are B & C
57 options remaining are A & D	15 options remaining are B & C
58 options remaining are B & C	16 options remaining are A & D
59 options remaining are B & C	17 options remaining are A & C
60 options remaining are B & C	18 options remaining are B & D
61 options remaining are A & C	19 options remaining are B & C
62 options remaining are A & B	20 options remaining are A & D
	21 options remaining are A & B
	22 options remaining are B & C
	23 options remaining are A & B
	24 options remaining are A & D
	25 options remaining are A & D
	26 options remaining are A & C
	27 options remaining are A & C
	28 options remaining are B & C
	29 options remaining are A & B
	30 options remaining are A & D
	31 options remaining are B & D
	32 options remaining are A & C
	33 options remaining are A & B
	34 options remaining are A & D
	35 options remaining are C & D
	36 options remaining are C & D
	37 options remaining are B & D
	38 options remaining are C & D
	39 options remaining are A & D
	40 options remaining are B & C
	41 options remaining are B & D
	42 options remaining are A & B

50:50

43 options remaining are A & C	1 options remaining are B & C
44 options remaining are A & C	2 options remaining are A & C
45 options remaining are C & D	3 options remaining are A & C
46 options remaining are A & D	4 options remaining are B & C
47 options remaining are C & D	5 options remaining are A & B
48 options remaining are A & D	6 options remaining are B & C
49 options remaining are A & B	7 options remaining are A & D
50 options remaining are A & B	8 options remaining are A & D
51 options remaining are A & B	9 options remaining are A & C
52 options remaining are B & C	10 options remaining are A & C
53 options remaining are C & D	11 options remaining are A & B
54 options remaining are C & D	12 options remaining are A & B
55 options remaining are A & B	13 options remaining are B & C
56 options remaining are B & D	14 options remaining are A & C
57 options remaining are C & D	15 options remaining are A & B
58 options remaining are C & D	16 options remaining are B & C
	17 options remaining are A & C
	18 options remaining are C & D
	19 options remaining are A & B
	20 options remaining are B & C
	21 options remaining are A & B
	22 options remaining are A & D
	23 options remaining are C & D
	24 options remaining are A & B
	25 options remaining are B & C
	26 options remaining are A & C
	27 options remaining are A & B
	28 options remaining are A & C
	29 options remaining are A & B
	30 options remaining are A & B
	31 options remaining are B & D
	32 options remaining are C & D
	33 options remaining are B & C
	34 options remaining are A & B
	35 options remaining are A & C
	36 options remaining are A & B
	37 options remaining are B & C
	38 options remaining are B & C
	39 options remaining are A & B
	40 options remaining are B & D
	41 options remaining are C & D
	42 options remaining are B & C

50:50

£125,000

43 options remaining are A & C	1 options remaining are A & B
44 options remaining are A & D	2 options remaining are A & C
45 options remaining are A & B	3 options remaining are A & B
46 options remaining are A & B	4 options remaining are A & B
	5 options remaining are A & B
	6 options remaining are A & B
	7 options remaining are B & D
	8 options remaining are A & D
	9 options remaining are A & D
	10 options remaining are C & D
	11 options remaining are A & B
	12 options remaining are B & D
	13 options remaining are A & B
	14 options remaining are A & C
	15 options remaining are B & D
	16 options remaining are A & C
	17 options remaining are A & B
	18 options remaining are A & D
	19 options remaining are B & D
	20 options remaining are A & B
	21 options remaining are A & D
	22 options remaining are C & D
	23 options remaining are A & B
	24 options remaining are A & D
	25 options remaining are C & D
	26 options remaining are A & C
	27 options remaining are B & D
	28 options remaining are B & D
	29 options remaining are C & D
	30 options remaining are A & B
	31 options remaining are B & C
	32 options remaining are A & B
	33 options remaining are B & D
	34 options remaining are B & C
	35 options remaining are B & C
	36 options remaining are A & D
	37 options remaining are B & C
	38 options remaining are A & D
	39 options remaining are A & B
	40 options remaining are B & D
	41 options remaining are A & B
	42 options remaining are A & B

50:50

£250,000

1 options remaining are A & C
2 options remaining are A & D
3 options remaining are B & D
4 options remaining are A & D
5 options remaining are A & B
6 options remaining are C & D
7 options remaining are A & B
8 options remaining are C & D
9 options remaining are B & C
10 options remaining are C & D
11 options remaining are B & C
12 options remaining are B & C
13 options remaining are B & C
14 options remaining are A & B
15 options remaining are A & B
16 options remaining are B & C
17 options remaining are B & D
18 options remaining are B & D
19 options remaining are A & D
20 options remaining are C & D
21 options remaining are B & D
22 options remaining are A & C
23 options remaining are B & C
24 options remaining are B & C
25 options remaining are A & B
26 options remaining are B & C
27 options remaining are B & D
28 options remaining are A & C
29 options remaining are B & C
30 options remaining are A & D
31 options remaining are A & C
32 options remaining are B & C
33 options remaining are A & B
34 options remaining are B & D
35 options remaining are B & C
36 options remaining are B & C
37 options remaining are A & C
38 options remaining are A & B

£500,000

1 options remaining are A & D
2 options remaining are A & D
3 options remaining are C & D
4 options remaining are B & C
5 options remaining are B & D
6 options remaining are B & C
7 options remaining are B & C
8 options remaining are B & C
9 options remaining are A & C
10 options remaining are A & D
11 options remaining are A & C
12 options remaining are B & D
13 options remaining are B & C
14 options remaining are A & C
15 options remaining are B & C
16 options remaining are A & C
17 options remaining are B & C
18 options remaining are C & D
19 options remaining are A & C
20 options remaining are A & C
21 options remaining are C & D
22 options remaining are B & C
23 options remaining are B & C
24 options remaining are B & C
25 options remaining are C & D
26 options remaining are A & C
27 options remaining are B & D
28 options remaining are A & C
29 options remaining are A & C
30 options remaining are A & C
31 options remaining are A & B
32 options remaining are B & D
33 options remaining are A & B
34 options remaining are A & D

50:50

£1,000,000

1   options remaining are B & D
2   options remaining are A & D
3   options remaining are A & C
4   options remaining are A & B
5   options remaining are A & D
6   options remaining are A & B
7   options remaining are A & D
8   options remaining are B & C
9   options remaining are C & D
10 options remaining are A & C
11 options remaining are A & B
12 options remaining are A & C
13 options remaining are B & C
14 options remaining are A & D
15 options remaining are A & B
16 options remaining are C & D
17 options remaining are A & C
18 options remaining are B & D
19 options remaining are A & D
20 options remaining are A & B
21 options remaining are B & D
22 options remaining are C & D
23 options remaining are A & B
24 options remaining are A & B
25 options remaining are B & D
26 options remaining are A & C
27 options remaining are A & B
28 options remaining are A & B
29 options remaining are C & D
30 options remaining are A & B

Answers

£100

1	A	2	B	3	B	4	A	5	B
6	A	7	A	8	B	9	A	10	D
11	C	12	A	13	A	14	B	15	C
16	C	17	A	18	C	19	C	20	B
21	A	22	A	23	B	24	B	25	C
26	A	27	C	28	D	29	C	30	D
31	C	32	C	33	D	34	A	35	C
36	B	37	D	38	A	39	A	40	D
41	A	42	B	43	B	44	C	45	B
46	A	47	A	48	D	49	B	50	A
51	B	52	B	53	B	54	D	55	A
56	D	57	D	58	B	59	A	60	D
61	D	62	C	63	C	64	B	65	A
66	D	67	C	68	D	69	C	70	B
71	A	72	C	73	A	74	A	75	C
76	B	77	B	78	D	79	A	80	A
81	A	82	B	83	D	84	D	85	B
86	D	87	C	88	A	89	A	90	D
91	A	92	C	93	D	94	A	95	C
96	D	97	C	98	B	99	B	100	B
101	B	102	D	103	C	104	D	105	A
106	A	107	D	108	B	109	D	110	B

If you have won £100, well done! Turn to page 33 to play for £200!

£200

1	A	2	D	3	B	4	D	5	A
6	B	7	A	8	B	9	B	10	D
11	C	12	D	13	A	14	B	15	C
16	C	17	C	18	D	19	D	20	D
21	A	22	B	23	C	24	A	25	A
26	C	27	D	28	D	29	B	30	D
31	B	32	C	33	A	34	D	35	A
36	A	37	A	38	D	39	B	40	B
41	A	42	C	43	C	44	B	45	D
46	D	47	B	48	C	49	D	50	D

ANSWERS

51 B	52 B	53 A	54 C	55 D
56 C	57 A	58 D	59 B	60 C
61 A	62 A	63 D	64 C	65 C
66 C	67 B	68 B	69 D	70 C
71 B	72 B	73 A	74 A	75 D
76 A	77 C	78 C	79 D	80 A
81 A	82 B	83 C	84 B	85 B
86 A	87 C	88 C	89 A	90 D
91 B	92 D	93 C	94 D	95 B
96 D	97 B	98 D		

If you have won £200, well done! Turn to page 55 to play for £300!

£300

1 B	2 C	3 C	4 C	5 A
6 D	7 D	8 A	9 A	10 D
11 A	12 C	13 D	14 C	15 A
16 C	17 B	18 D	19 B	20 D
21 D	22 D	23 D	24 B	25 B
26 D	27 C	28 C	29 B	30 B
31 C	32 B	33 D	34 B	35 D
36 C	37 D	38 B	39 C	40 A
41 B	42 D	43 B	44 B	45 C
46 A	47 B	48 B	49 B	50 C
51 C	52 C	53 A	54 B	55 C
56 D	57 A	58 B	59 B	60 D
61 C	62 D	63 A	64 B	65 D
66 C	67 B	68 C	69 D	70 B
71 A	72 B	73 C	74 B	75 B
76 B	77 A	78 B	79 C	80 A
81 B	82 A	83 C	84 A	85 D
86 B	87 B	88 A	89 B	90 D
91 B	92 C	93 D	94 C	

If you have won £300, well done! Turn to page 75 to play for £500!

ANSWERS

£500

1 D	2 D	3 A	4 C	5 C
6 C	7 A	8 A	9 C	10 A
11 C	12 D	13 B	14 A	15 D
16 B	17 C	18 B	19 C	20 C
21 A	22 D	23 A	24 B	25 D
26 A	27 B	28 A	29 B	30 D
31 A	32 A	33 B	34 B	35 A
36 C	37 B	38 B	39 B	40 D
41 A	42 B	43 B	44 B	45 D
46 C	47 C	48 C	49 B	50 B
51 B	52 D	53 C	54 B	55 A
56 B	57 B	58 A	59 B	60 C
61 C	62 A	63 C	64 C	65 D
66 A	67 A	68 C	69 B	70 B
71 A	72 D	73 B	74 D	75 D
76 C	77 C	78 B	79 A	80 B
81 C	82 D	83 B	84 D	85 B
86 C	87 B	88 A	89 C	90 B

If you have won £500, well done! Turn to page 95 to play for £1,000!

£1,000

1 D	2 D	3 B	4 A	5 B
6 C	7 C	8 C	9 D	10 C
11 C	12 C	13 C	14 D	15 D
16 B	17 A	18 B	19 C	20 B
21 B	22 D	23 B	24 B	25 B
26 A	27 D	28 C	29 D	30 D
31 B	32 B	33 A	34 C	35 B
36 D	37 C	38 B	39 A	40 B
41 A	42 D	43 A	44 D	45 A
46 D	47 B	48 A	49 D	50 A
51 B	52 B	53 C	54 C	55 B
56 D	57 A	58 B	59 A	60 A
61 C	62 A	63 C	64 B	65 B
66 A	67 B	68 D	69 A	70 B
71 D	72 D	73 B	74 B	75 C
76 C	77 C	78 B	79 B	80 A
81 A	82 B	83 C	84 A	85 C
86 B				

If you have won £1,000, well done! Turn to page 115 to play for £2,000!

ANSWERS

£2,000

1 C	2 D	3 A	4 D	5 B
6 D	7 B	8 D	9 C	10 A
11 A	12 B	13 B	14 C	15 A
16 D	17 C	18 A	19 C	20 B
21 C	22 B	23 B	24 C	25 C
26 B	27 A	28 B	29 A	30 A
31 D	32 D	33 B	34 C	35 A
36 B	37 B	38 D	39 B	40 B
41 C	42 B	43 B	44 B	45 C
46 D	47 D	48 A	49 A	50 D
51 D	52 D	53 D	54 C	55 B
56 C	57 C	58 A	59 D	60 C
61 C	62 A	63 A	64 A	65 C
66 D	67 D	68 B	69 B	70 D
71 D	72 D	73 B	74 C	

If you have won £2,000, well done! Turn to page 131 to play for £4,000!

£4,000

1 D	2 A	3 D	4 D	5 C
6 D	7 C	8 D	9 B	10 B
11 C	12 A	13 B	14 A	15 B
16 B	17 C	18 D	19 D	20 B
21 B	22 A	23 B	24 D	25 D
26 A	27 B	28 D	29 C	30 D
31 B	32 D	33 D	34 B	35 D
36 D	37 D	38 A	39 B	40 B
41 A	42 D	43 A	44 A	45 C
46 A	47 D	48 B	49 D	50 A
51 C	52 A	53 A	54 D	55 C
56 D	57 C	58 A	59 C	60 D
61 A	62 B	63 D	64 C	65 A
66 A	67 A	68 A	69 C	70 B

If you have won £4,000, well done! Turn to page 147 to play for £8,000!

ANSWERS

£8,000

1 A	2 D	3 B	4 C	5 A
6 D	7 D	8 C	9 A	10 D
11 D	12 C	13 B	14 B	15 B
16 D	17 C	18 B	19 B	20 A
21 A	22 B	23 D	24 D	25 A
26 A	27 D	28 A	29 D	30 B
31 B	32 D	33 A	34 A	35 A
36 D	37 D	38 B	39 C	40 D
41 A	42 A	43 C	44 C	45 B
46 D	47 C	48 C	49 B	50 B
51 D	52 D	53 D	54 A	55 C
56 B	57 C	58 A	59 C	60 D
61 D	62 B	63 A	64 A	65 A
66 A				

If you have won £8,000, well done! Turn to page 163 to play for £16,000!

£16,000

1 A	2 A	3 A	4 C	5 A
6 D	7 B	8 B	9 A	10 B
11 B	12 C	13 A	14 C	15 B
16 B	17 A	18 A	19 A	20 A
21 D	22 A	23 C	24 B	25 A
26 B	27 B	28 C	29 B	30 D
31 D	32 C	33 A	34 D	35 C
36 D	37 B	38 B	39 D	40 B
41 A	42 D	43 D	44 B	45 B
46 C	47 C	48 B	49 C	50 D
51 B	52 B	53 A	54 A	55 C
56 D	57 D	58 B	59 B	60 B
61 C	62 A			

If you have won £16,000, well done! Turn to page 177 to play for £32,000!

ANSWERS

£32,000

1 B	2 A	3 B	4 B	5 D
6 B	7 D	8 A	9 A	10 D
11 C	12 C	13 C	14 B	15 C
16 D	17 A	18 D	19 C	20 D
21 A	22 B	23 A	24 D	25 D
26 C	27 C	28 B	29 A	30 D
31 D	32 C	33 A	34 A	35 C
36 D	37 B	38 C	39 A	40 C
41 B	42 A	43 C	44 C	45 D
46 A	47 D	48 A	49 A	50 A
51 B	52 B	53 C	54 C	55 A
56 D	57 C	58 D		

If you have won £32,000, well done! Turn to page 191 to play for £64,000!

£64,000

1 B	2 A	3 C	4 B	5 A
6 C	7 A	8 A	9 C	10 A
11 B	12 A	13 C	14 A	15 A
16 C	17 A	18 C	19 B	20 C
21 A	22 D	23 C	24 A	25 B
26 C	27 A	28 A	29 A	30 A
31 D	32 C	33 B	34 A	35 C
36 B	37 B	38 B	39 B	40 D
41 C	42 B	43 C	44 A	45 A
46 A				

If you have won £64,000, well done! Turn to page 203 to play for £125,000!

£125,000

1 A	2 A	3 A	4 B	5 B
6 B	7 D	8 A	9 D	10 D
11 B	12 B	13 A	14 A	15 B
16 A	17 A	18 D	19 D	20 B
21 A	22 D	23 B	24 D	25 C
26 A	27 B	28 D	29 D	30 A
31 B	32 B	33 D	34 B	35 B
36 D	37 B	38 D	39 B	40 D
41 B	42 A			

If you have won £125,000, well done! Turn to page 213 to play for £250,000!

ANSWERS

£250,000

1 C	2 D	3 D	4 D	5 A
6 D	7 B	8 D	9 B	10 C
11 C	12 B	13 C	14 A	15 A
16 B	17 B	18 B	19 A	20 D
21 D	22 C	23 C	24 C	25 B
26 B	27 D	28 C	29 B	30 D
31 C	32 C	33 A	34 B	35 C
36 C	37 A	38 B		

If you have won £250,000, well done! Turn to page 223 to play for £500,000!

£500,000

1 A	2 D	3 C	4 C	5 D
6 C	7 C	8 B	9 A	10 A
11 C	12 B	13 B	14 A	15 C
16 A	17 C	18 D	19 A	20 C
21 D	22 B	23 B	24 C	25 D
26 A	27 D	28 A	29 C	30 C
31 B	32 D	33 A	34 A	

If you have won £500,000, well done! Turn to page 231 to play for £1,000,000!

£1,000,000

1 D	2 D	3 A	4 A	5 A
6 B	7 D	8 D	9 C	10 C
11 B	12 A	13 C	14 A	15 B
16 D	17 C	18 D	19 A	20 B
21 B	22 C	23 A	24 B	25 D
26 A	27 A	28 A	29 C	30 A

If you have won £1,000,000, well done! You're a millionaire!

Score sheets

Write your name and the names of any other contestants in the space provided. Shade in each of the boxes lightly with a pencil once you or one of your fellow contestants has won the amount in that box. If you or any of the other contestants answer a question incorrectly and are out of the game, use a soft eraser to rub out the relevant boxes so that the final score is showing.

SCORE SHEET

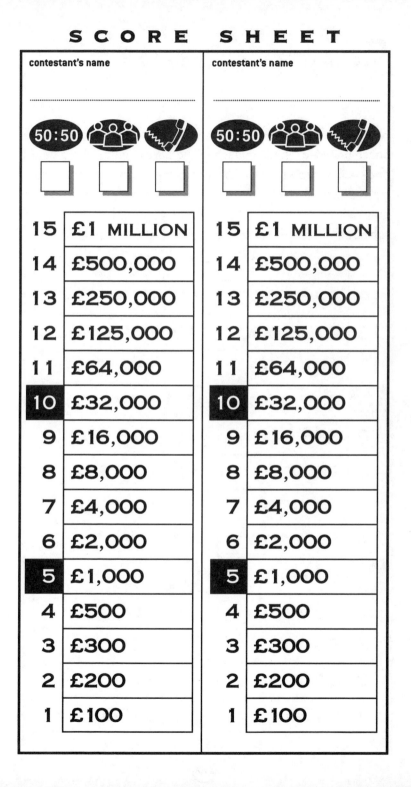

contestant's name		contestant's name	
....		....	
50:50 👥 📞		50:50 👥 📞	
☐ ☐ ☐		☐ ☐ ☐	
15	£1 MILLION	15	£1 MILLION
14	£500,000	14	£500,000
13	£250,000	13	£250,000
12	£125,000	12	£125,000
11	£64,000	11	£64,000
10	£32,000	10	£32,000
9	£16,000	9	£16,000
8	£8,000	8	£8,000
7	£4,000	7	£4,000
6	£2,000	6	£2,000
5	£1,000	5	£1,000
4	£500	4	£500
3	£300	3	£300
2	£200	2	£200
1	£100	1	£100

SCORE SHEET

contestant's name	contestant's name
....	....

50:50	👥	☎		50:50	👥	☎
☐	☐	☐		☐	☐	☐

15	£1 MILLION		15	£1 MILLION
14	£500,000		14	£500,000
13	£250,000		13	£250,000
12	£125,000		12	£125,000
11	£64,000		11	£64,000
10	£32,000		**10**	£32,000
9	£16,000		9	£16,000
8	£8,000		8	£8,000
7	£4,000		7	£4,000
6	£2,000		6	£2,000
5	£1,000		**5**	£1,000
4	£500		4	£500
3	£300		3	£300
2	£200		2	£200
1	£100		1	£100

SCORE SHEET

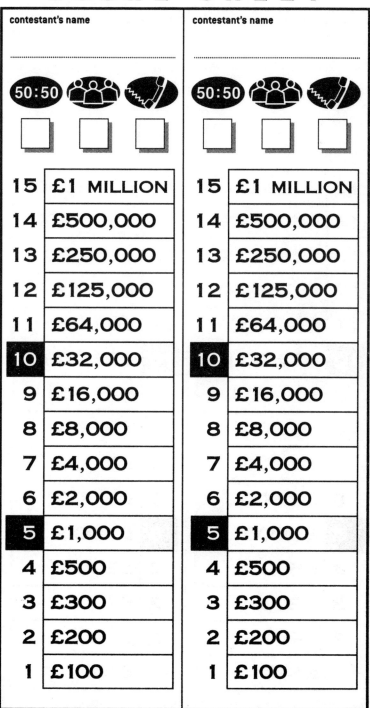

S C O R E   S H E E T

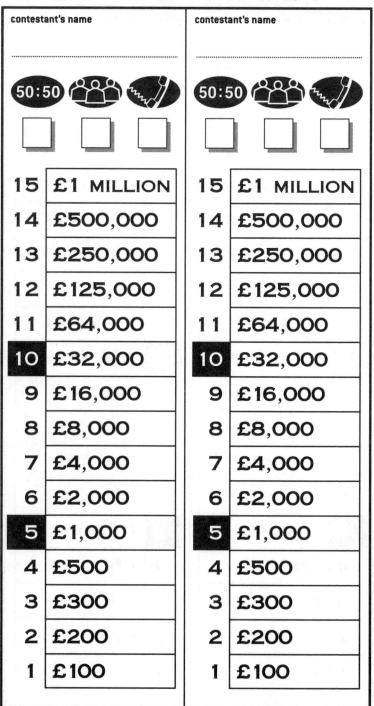

contestant's name	contestant's name
....	....

50:50	👥	☎	50:50	👥	☎
☐	☐	☐	☐	☐	☐

15	£1 MILLION	15	£1 MILLION
14	£500,000	14	£500,000
13	£250,000	13	£250,000
12	£125,000	12	£125,000
11	£64,000	11	£64,000
10	£32,000	10	£32,000
9	£16,000	9	£16,000
8	£8,000	8	£8,000
7	£4,000	7	£4,000
6	£2,000	6	£2,000
5	£1,000	5	£1,000
4	£500	4	£500
3	£300	3	£300
2	£200	2	£200
1	£100	1	£100

SCORE SHEET

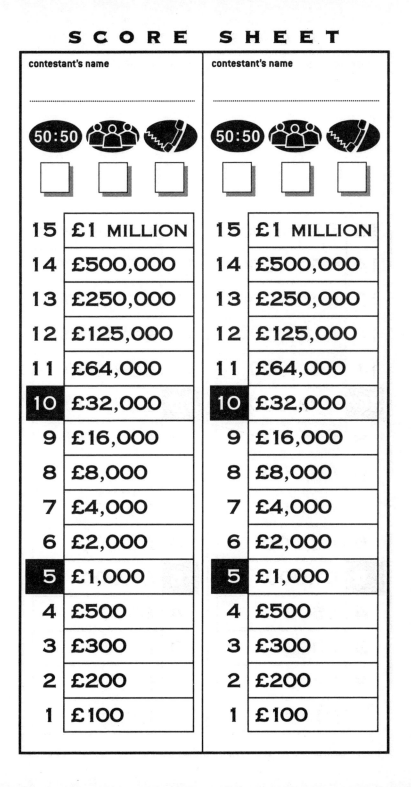

contestant's name			contestant's name	
....			....	

| 50:50 | | | 50:50 | |

15	£1 MILLION	15	£1 MILLION
14	£500,000	14	£500,000
13	£250,000	13	£250,000
12	£125,000	12	£125,000
11	£64,000	11	£64,000
10	£32,000	10	£32,000
9	£16,000	9	£16,000
8	£8,000	8	£8,000
7	£4,000	7	£4,000
6	£2,000	6	£2,000
5	£1,000	5	£1,000
4	£500	4	£500
3	£300	3	£300
2	£200	2	£200
1	£100	1	£100

SCORE SHEET

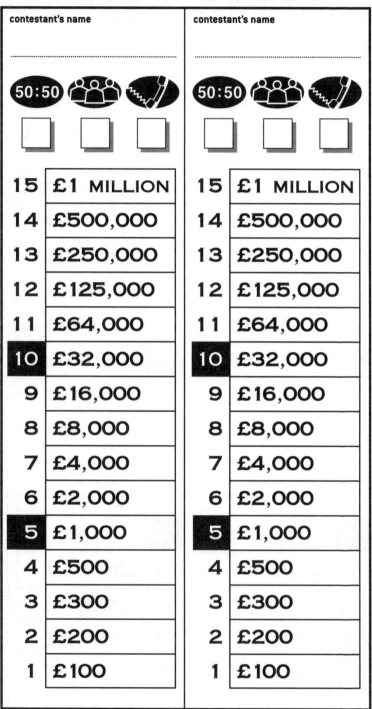

contestant's name	contestant's name
....	....

	50:50	👥	☎		50:50	👥	☎
	☐	☐	☐		☐	☐	☐

15	£1 MILLION	15	£1 MILLION
14	£500,000	14	£500,000
13	£250,000	13	£250,000
12	£125,000	12	£125,000
11	£64,000	11	£64,000
10	£32,000	10	£32,000
9	£16,000	9	£16,000
8	£8,000	8	£8,000
7	£4,000	7	£4,000
6	£2,000	6	£2,000
5	£1,000	5	£1,000
4	£500	4	£500
3	£300	3	£300
2	£200	2	£200
1	£100	1	£100

SCORE SHEET

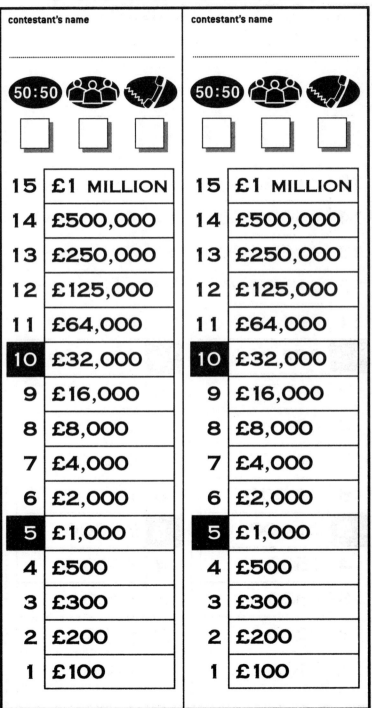

contestant's name	contestant's name
50:50 ☐ people ☐ phone ☐	50:50 ☐ people ☐ phone ☐

15	£1 MILLION	15	£1 MILLION
14	£500,000	14	£500,000
13	£250,000	13	£250,000
12	£125,000	12	£125,000
11	£64,000	11	£64,000
10	£32,000	10	£32,000
9	£16,000	9	£16,000
8	£8,000	8	£8,000
7	£4,000	7	£4,000
6	£2,000	6	£2,000
5	£1,000	5	£1,000
4	£500	4	£500
3	£300	3	£300
2	£200	2	£200
1	£100	1	£100

SCORE SHEET

contestant's name		contestant's name	
....		....	

50:50 👥 ☎		50:50 👥 ☎	
☐ ☐ ☐		☐ ☐ ☐	

15	£1 MILLION	15	£1 MILLION
14	£500,000	14	£500,000
13	£250,000	13	£250,000
12	£125,000	12	£125,000
11	£64,000	11	£64,000
10	£32,000	**10**	£32,000
9	£16,000	9	£16,000
8	£8,000	8	£8,000
7	£4,000	7	£4,000
6	£2,000	6	£2,000
5	£1,000	**5**	£1,000
4	£500	4	£500
3	£300	3	£300
2	£200	2	£200
1	£100	1	£100

SCORE SHEET

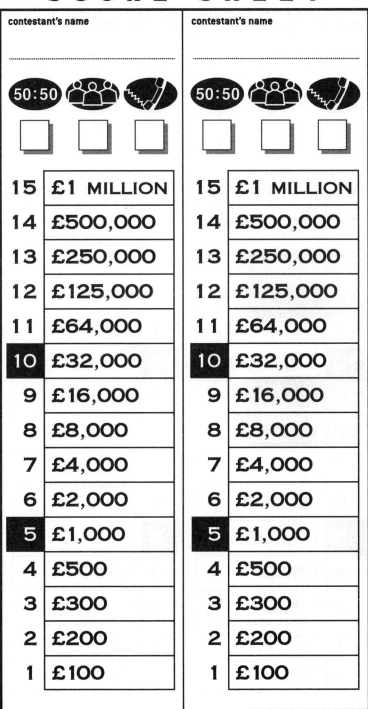

contestant's name		contestant's name	
....		....	
15	£1 MILLION	15	£1 MILLION
14	£500,000	14	£500,000
13	£250,000	13	£250,000
12	£125,000	12	£125,000
11	£64,000	11	£64,000
10	£32,000	10	£32,000
9	£16,000	9	£16,000
8	£8,000	8	£8,000
7	£4,000	7	£4,000
6	£2,000	6	£2,000
5	£1,000	5	£1,000
4	£500	4	£500
3	£300	3	£300
2	£200	2	£200
1	£100	1	£100

SCORE SHEET

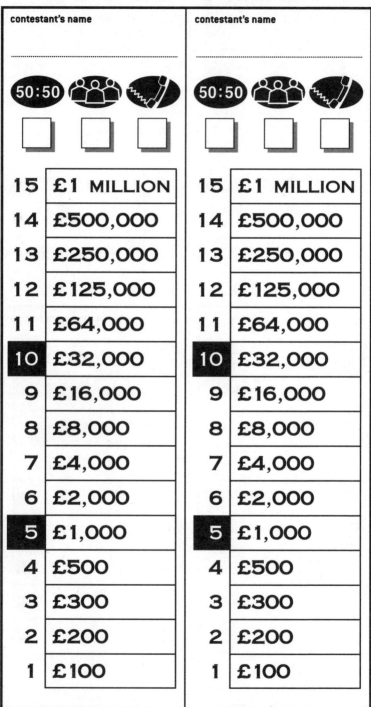

contestant's name		contestant's name	
....		....	
50:50 👥 📞		50:50 👥 📞	
☐ ☐ ☐		☐ ☐ ☐	
15	£1 MILLION	15	£1 MILLION
14	£500,000	14	£500,000
13	£250,000	13	£250,000
12	£125,000	12	£125,000
11	£64,000	11	£64,000
10	£32,000	10	£32,000
9	£16,000	9	£16,000
8	£8,000	8	£8,000
7	£4,000	7	£4,000
6	£2,000	6	£2,000
5	£1,000	5	£1,000
4	£500	4	£500
3	£300	3	£300
2	£200	2	£200
1	£100	1	£100